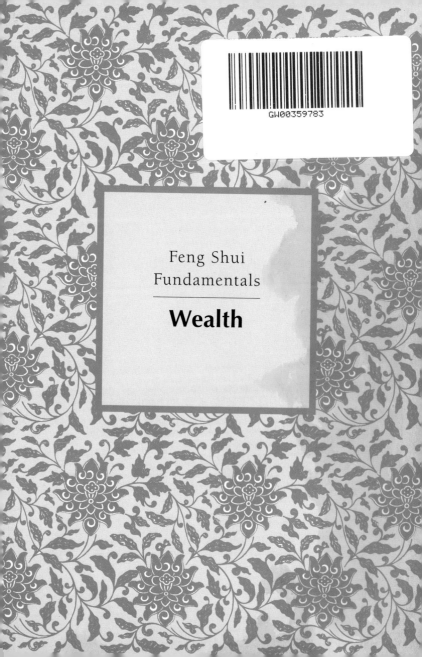

Feng Shui
Fundamentals

Wealth

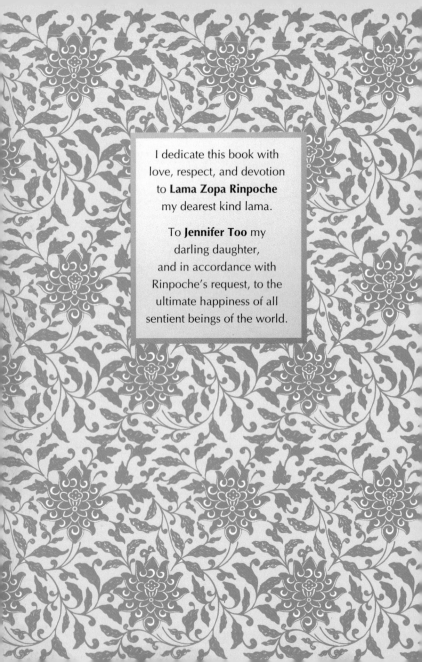

I dedicate this book with
love, respect, and devotion
to **Lama Zopa Rinpoche**
my dearest kind lama.

To **Jennifer Too** my
darling daughter,
and in accordance with
Rinpoche's request, to the
ultimate happiness of all
sentient beings of the world.

Feng Shui
Fundamentals

Wealth

Lillian Too

ELEMENT

Shaftesbury, Dorset • Rockport, Massachusetts • Melbourne, Victoria

© Element Books Limited 1997
Text © Lillian Too 1997

First published in Great Britain by
ELEMENT BOOKS LIMITED
Shaftesbury, Dorset SP7 8BP

Published in the USA in 1997 by
ELEMENT BOOKS INC.
PO Box 830, Rockport, MA 01966

Published in Australia in 1997 by
ELEMENT BOOKS LIMITED
and distributed by Penguin Australia Ltd
487 Maroondah Highway, Ringwood, Victoria 3134

Designed and created with
THE BRIDGEWATER BOOK COMPANY LIMITED

ELEMENT BOOKS LIMITED
Editorial Director Julia McCutchen
Managing Editor Caro Ness
Production Director Roger Lane
Production Sarah Golden

THE BRIDGEWATER BOOK COMPANY LIMITED
Art Director Terry Jeavons
Designer James Lawrence
Managing Editor Anne Townley
Project Editor Andrew Kirk
Editor Linda Doeser
Picture Research Julia Hanson
Studio Photography Guy Ryecart
Illustrations Isabel Rayner, Andrew Kulman, Mark Jamieson,
Michaela Blunden, Paul Collicutt, Olivia Rayner, Jackie Harland

Printed and bound in Hong Kong

British Library Cataloguing in Publication Data available

Library of Congress Cataloging in Publication data available

ISBN 1 86204 118 0

The publishers wish to thank the following for the use of pictures:
Elizabeth Whiting Associates, pp 16, 19, 26; Image Bank, pp 6, 14, 15, 18/19, 48;
Wolfgang Kaehler/Corbis, p 13; Rex, p 27; and Zefa, p 37.

Special thanks go to:
Bright Ideas, Lewes, East Sussex
for help with properties

Lillian Too's website addresses are
http://www.asiaconnect.com.my/lillian-too
http://www.dragonmagic.com

Lillian Too's email addresses are
ltoo@dragonmagic.com
ltoo@popmail.asiaconnect.com.my

CONTENTS

INTRODUCTION

THE TRINITY OF LUCK

風
水

The Chinese traditionally believe that the material well-being of people is governed by three types of luck, tien ti ren, that emanate in equal measure from heaven, earth, and the individual self.

Heaven luck is beyond the control of humans. Commonly referred to as fate, or in other cultures as karma, heaven luck determines the circumstances of our birth and our destiny. There are many different theories that address this aspect of human existence, but the Chinese believe it is mainly heaven luck that determines if an individual is destined for greatness or doomed to obscurity, whether he or she is born rich or poor and whether the journey through life will bring wealth and repute or misfortune and tragedy. We can forewarn ourselves by attempting to learn more about our destiny through divination, but many believe that the luck from heaven is difficult to change.

Feng shui wisdom also allows for earth luck and human luck which, unlike heaven luck, is within our control, and which if properly activated, may alter our fate.

The Chinese believe that heaven luck is largely predetermined. However, we may forewarn ourselves by visiting a clairvoyant or by other methods of divination.

FENG SHUI TAPS THE LUCK OF THE EARTH

Earth luck is feng shui. Live harmoniously with the energies of the earth and its invisible forces, termed sheng chi, or the cosmic breath of the dragon, will bring you great good fortune. Earth luck helps you to enhance good heaven luck, thus expanding the scale of your successes during good times, and bringing you good fortune and prosperity.

It also modifies inauspicious heaven luck, helping you overcome difficulties and loss during astrological bad times. Good earth luck often helps you avoid ruin and misfortune caused either by unfavorable human luck (your own stupid actions), or unlucky periods in your natal charts. Feng shui provides you with simple advice on how to adapt and protect your immediate living area, thereby deflecting any misfortune that may be coming your way.

While fate is at the core of feng shui, practitioners still contend that our fate can be modified, changed, and even enhanced, depending on the circumstances of our earth luck. In the same way, our determination to activate our own individual human luck will also affect our fortunes.

The Chinese are believers in the theory of the superior man as laid out in the great classic, the I Ching, or Book of Changes. The tenets of feng shui practice, based on the I Ching, therefore dictate that the indi-

Tap the luck of the earth to bring forth the cosmic breath of the dragon and ensure good fortune.

vidual's noble and moral conduct will have a significant effect on his or her destiny and on the outcome of any enterprise or endeavor that person undertakes.

The practice of feng shui must always be viewed in the context of the fundamental philosophy of the trinity of luck. Tien, Ti, and Ren choy – heaven, earth, and human luck – together dictate our destinies on earth.

THE CHINESE VIEW OF WEALTH

Becoming rich and prosperous is an almost universal aspiration of the Chinese people. They make no secret of this fact. Material possessions are a primary consideration if you wish to be seen as a success, and the Chinese pre-occupation with prosperity is reflected in many of their cultural practices.

The Chinese greeting when they see someone is seldom, "Hello, how are you?" but "Are you well, have you eaten?" This preoccupation with eating has its roots in material welfare. The rice bowl is often symbolic of this well-being, so there are those who regard a golden rice bowl as signifying wealth.

The Chinese send red or gold cards during the New Year festival.

A golden rice bowl symbolizes wealth.

During the lunar New Year celebrations – the most important annual festival – the Chinese send cards that are always printed in red (to signify an auspicious occasion) or gold (to signify wealth) and the greeting is always Kung Hei Fatt Choy, or "congratulations and may you become more prosperous". The Chinese New Year greeting never wavers from these four words.

For the Chinese, wishing friends and loved ones prosperity during the New Year is considered an important part of the celebrations. The Chinese never visit each other's homes empty-handed; they always bring some "gold" along. One favorite present is the gift of mandarin oranges because they signify kum, or gold, once again encouraging wealth in to the home.

There are other symbols of prosperity used during the 15 days of the Chinese New Year – either displayed at home as part of the New Year feng shui or sent as gifts to close friends and relatives, including the following:

- ▧ The pineapple fruit, which indicates that good luck is coming.
- ▧ A pair of potted lime plants dripping with orange fruits, which signifies wealth luck.
- ▧ A potted jade plant to wish the recipient great prosperity.

The pineapple is often displayed as a symbol of good luck during the Chinese New Year.

This book focuses exclusively on the wealth-generating aspects of feng shui and has not proved difficult to write because there are so many symbols, so many different methods, and so many ways of activating wealth feng shui. Just remember that the effectiveness of the methods presented here will work differently for different people, depending on other factors, particularly the balance of the individual's Tien Ti Ren luck.

The pursuit of material wealth represents such a big part of the Chinese psyche that many feng shui guidelines focus on it. The promise of prosperity is probably what has kept the practice of feng shui alive all these centuries. Passed on from father to son, prosperity feng shui continues to be practiced by modern day descendants.

BALANCE

When you practice feng shui, do not worry if you cannot act upon every suggestion. More is not necessarily always better. Balance is vital. Sometimes just energizing one method or activating one auspicious direction may be sufficient. An excellent indicator that your feng shui is working is when you find yourself suddenly becoming very busy. Good feng shui brings opportunity, but for this to crystallize into wealth, you will have to work at making full use of the luck that has come your way.

~ 9 ~

THE CHINESE GODS OF WEALTH

Many Chinese homes display gods of wealth. These deities are seldom worshipped in a religious fashion, but displayed in rooms and offices to symbolize the importance of the wealth aspiration. If you wish to do the same, you can find them in a Chinese supermarket in any major Western city.

FUK, LUK, AND SAU

The most popular are the three star gods, collectively referred to as Fuk, Luk, and Sau, which literally translated means wealth, affluence, and longevity. They are present in almost all Chinese homes and are believed to bring great good luck to households, especially wealth luck.

Fuk, Luk, and Sau always stand alongside one another.

▨ Luk, the god of high rank and affluence, holds the scepter of power and authority. He stands on the right.

▨ Fuk symbolizes happiness and wealth, stands a head taller, and is placed in the center.

▨ Sau, with his domed head and carrying a peach in one hand and a walking stick in the other, is often accompanied by a deer and stands on the left.

Wealthy Chinese families in Hong Kong, Taiwan, and Singapore often commission specially crafted giant-sized figurines of **Fuk, Luk, and Sau** to display in special rooms designed to house them. Middle class families buy ceramic, enamel, or wooden replicas and these are believed to be just as symbolically effective.

OTHER PERSONIFICATIONS OF WEALTH

There are a number of other deities who are believed to bring wealth luck into households.

The laughing Buddha.

THE LAUGHING BUDDHA

This is an extremely popular deity with business people. This fat Buddha, with a broadly smiling face and a huge fat belly, can often be seen, usually in standing form, in restaurants and jewelry stores. The laughing Buddha is also portrayed fanning himself while seated on a bag of gold (depicting wealth), or surrounded by a group of five children.

TSAI SHEN YEH

Popular with the Cantonese, this is another prosperity god. He has a fierce countenance and he is seated on a tiger. If you place him directly facing the main door, wealth will be attracted into the home.

KUAN KUNG

Also known as Kuan Ti, Kuan Kung is a popular deity. He is said to bring both prosperity and protection, and is also the powerful god of war. The story of Kuan Kung is documented in the Romance of the Three Kingdoms. Displaying his fierce countenance in the living room, preferably facing the main door, is sufficient to attract good fortune.

Kuan Kung.

WONG CHOY SAN

Another popular wealth deity, he is widely believed to be extremely generous to households that display him. He is often depicted carrying a rat, with gold bars placed at his feet.

Wong Choy San.

WEALTH FENG SHUI

USING THE PA KUA

財富

Understanding the Pa Kua, which is the principal symbol of feng shui practice, is the first step toward achieving wealth luck. There are two arrangements of the Pa Kua, known as the Early Heaven and the Later Heaven. The former arrangement is believed to be a powerful protective tool and hanging it above the main door outside the home is deemed sufficient to deflect any negative energies that may be threatening the home.

However, the Later Heaven Pa Kua, with its multiple concentric rings, is a reference tool for analysis and there is profound symbolic meaning in each of the characters that appear on each side of it. In addition, every corner of this eight-sided emblem is represented by a trigram, and each trigram offers further symbols and meanings for feng shui interpretation.

Trigrams are three-lined symbols. These lines may either be solid yang lines or broken yin lines. The relationship between these lines is what gives meanings to the trigrams, according to the ancient Chinese text called the I Ching or Book of Changes.

THE DIRECTION SOUTHEAST

The trigram that represents the prosperity aspiration is Sun and, according to the Later Heaven Arrangement, it is placed in the southeast. This

is therefore the corner of the home or office that represents wealth, and if this corner has good feng shui, then the wealth aspirations of the household have been effectively energized. If this corner has bad feng shui, however, inauspicious money luck will befall the household, leading to loss and failure in business. To activate wealth feng shui it is therefore vital to ensure that any negative energy is removed or deflected from the southeast corner of your home or office.

SUN

This trigram has two solid yang lines above a broken yin line, which signifies the wind that brings prosperity. The image conjured by this trigram is of the wind scattering seeds to all corners of the earth. The seeds then fall to the ground, penetrate the soil, and begin to germinate. Very soon a plant grows. It blooms and flowers, producing more seeds, which are scattered again by the wind, and the cycle of prosperity is repeated over and over again. Thus is wealth creation symbolized. If you activate this trigram in your home, it is believed that all your financial projects will succeed.

PRODUCTIVE CYCLE

This illustration shows the productive cycle of the five elements - earth, metal, water, wood, and fire. Water, the element that produces wood, is in a positive position in relation to wood and is therefore helping to energize wood, which is associated with wealth and prosperity.

APPLYING THE THEORY OF ELEMENT ANALYSIS

The best method of energizing the southeast, thereby activating prosperity luck for the residents of your home, is to apply the theory of the five elements. According to the classical texts, all things in the universe, tangible or intangible, belong to one of five elements. These are fire, wood, water, metal, and earth. They are said to interact with each other in never-ending productive and destructive cycles. Applying element analysis to feng shui requires a full understanding of how the cycles work and how they may be applied in a practical way.

THE WOOD ELEMENT

The element of the southeast location is wood, symbolized by plants and all things made of wood, and this is most significant when practicing feng shui, since identifying the relevant and applicable element to activate is vital to the process. It suggests that placing a plant in the southeast, for instance, will be excellent wealth feng shui. Moreover, from the cycles shown here, you will see further attributes of the wood element.

- Wood is produced by water, so it will benefit from water.
- Wood itself produces fire, so fire will exhaust it.
- Wood is destroyed by metal, so metal will harm it.
- Wood destroys earth, so it will overwhelm earth.

From studying these attributes we learn that to energize the element of the southeast we should use all objects that symbolize both the wood and water elements, and we should avoid anything belonging to the metal element.

If we delve a little deeper into element analysis, we discover that the southeast is represented by small wood. This in itself suggests to us the kind of wood we should use to activate this corner, and implies that although water is good for wood, there should not be so much of it that it will drown it. Further study will show that, while fire exhausts wood, without its warmth plants cannot blossom and there can be no harvest. Finally, although wood is destroyed by metal, the value of wood can be enhanced by the use of small metal, such as implements and tools made of steel that transform the raw material into tables and chairs. It is important to remember that in feng shui balance is everything. There should never be too much of any one element as this will overwhelm the other elements. If all five elements are used subtly they will supplement and reinforce each other.

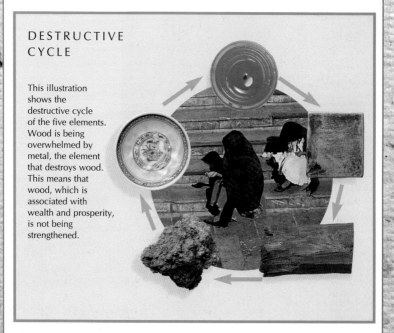

DESTRUCTIVE CYCLE

This illustration shows the destructive cycle of the five elements. Wood is being overwhelmed by metal, the element that destroys wood. This means that wood, which is associated with wealth and prosperity, is not being strengthened.

ENERGIZING THE WOOD ELEMENT

In feng shui, each of the five elements is activated when objects belonging to that particular element group are present. To energize the wood element of the southeast wealth corner, the sector known as "small wood," the best method is to use as many plants as possible, especially small ones. Almost any kind of plant will do, as long as they look healthy and vigorous. For this reason you can even use artificial plants if you like. However, some plants are more auspicious than others, while some are not recommended at all.

GOOD-FORTUNE PLANTS

Feng shui always recommends the use of broad-leaved plants that look healthy and green. If flowering plants or cut flowers are used, they should always look fresh and bright. Sickly or dead-looking plants and flowers emit a negative energy that signifies loss. You should therefore never use dried flowers in this corner. If a plant starts to wilt, throw it out and replace it immediately with healthier-looking plants.

The Chinese jade plant is highly recommended. It has succulent leaves that

Plants should always look healthy and green. If a plant is in poor health, replace it with a healthier specimen.

Avoid plants with thorns or spines, such as these cacti, as they are inauspicious.

COLORS

The wood element is also activated by using green and brown colors – in any shade or hue. Drapes, duvets, carpets, and wallpapers in the southeast should be predominantly greens or browns. You can be as creative as you like when implementing the suggestions here and they are by no means exclusive. Some people use paintings of lush green scenery to activate this corner, others use wooden paneling. Whatever you use, do not overdo it. Balance is vital.

suggest wealth. Affluent Chinese homes display an ornamental plant made from real jade to stimulate prosperity.

The oriental lime plant covered with lots of fruits symbolizes a successful harvest. If this is not available, an orange tree may also be used or an artificial plant. The oranges suggest a tree ripe with gold. It is a most auspicious energizer to display in the home.

INAUSPICIOUS PLANTS

Avoid displaying stunted or deformed plants, such as bonsai or cactus. Although these look quaint and can be exquisitely beautiful, the suggestion of stunted development is not good. Auspicious feng shui always suggests abundant growth.

OTHER OBJECTS

In addition to plants and flowers, other objects made of wood can also be placed in the southeast, but a living plant is always to be preferred. Never have dried or dying plants or driftwood in this corner. Their energy is enervating in a corner that needs plenty of life.

Keep an aquarium with goldfish to attract wealth luck.

USING OBJECTS OF THE WATER ELEMENT

Applying the theory of the productive cycle of the elements indicates that water produces wood, so water features will also activate the southeast to attract wealth luck. Throughout history water has always represented wealth to the Chinese. Many Chinese restaurants use the water element to improve the feng shui of their premises by drawing a fish or water motif around their walls.

This motif can also be drawn on the southeast walls of your living room or, as the Chinese do, you can buy a miniature fountain that keeps the water flowing in a never-ending cycle. This small movement of water is considered most auspicious and, when used in stores and offices, it often represents good luck in increasing turnover. A well-lit aquarium with goldfish is also a good idea. The bubbling oxygenators represent excellent feng shui. If you keep fish, make sure there are nine, of which eight should be red or gold and one black. The black fish will absorb any bad luck that inadvertently enters the corner. It is most auspicious to

keep arrowanas – a tropical fish that is universally acknowledged as the best feng shui fish.

If your room is large or you wish to activate water in the southeast of your garden for wealth luck, you can be very ambitious and install any one of the following water features.

- A small fish pond filled with good-fortune carp, as long as it is to the left of your front door.
- A small waterfall, which, if it also happens to face the front door of your home, is considered so auspicious as to bring you enormous wealth luck.

Artificial waterfalls are extremely popular with the Chinese in southeast Asia, and many have had their bank balances expanded after installing such a garden feature. Again take note of balance. Do not have a waterfall that is so large as to overwhelm the house.

A small artificial waterfall in the garden is extremely auspicious.

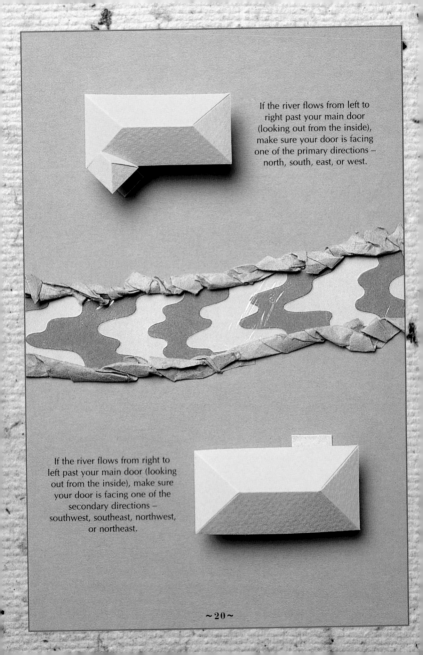

If the river flows from left to right past your main door (looking out from the inside), make sure your door is facing one of the primary directions – north, south, east, or west.

If the river flows from right to left past your main door (looking out from the inside), make sure your door is facing one of the secondary directions – southwest, southeast, northwest, or northeast.

ACTIVATING BIG AND SMALL WATER

Water feng shui is a fascinating subject and because it symbolizes money, there are advanced formulas devoted exclusively to its treatment, its direction of flow, and its exit and entrance directions. These are based on the Water Dragon Classic. The formulas differentiate between big water – natural bodies of water, such as rivers and lakes – and small or artificial water. Both bring wealth but big water brings more.

Those fortunate enough to live near such water are very lucky and all that is required to tap the awesome good luck of the river or lake is to orient your main door in the correct way. This is summarized in the diagram shown here.

If you do not live anywhere near a natural body of water, you can simulate its lucky energies by using the humble drain that surrounds your home. This is artificially activating small water. Design your drain so that it flows past your entrance door in the correct direction.

Living in an apartment that faces a river is also very good feng shui. Try to keep windows that have a view of the river perpetually open or build a mirror on one of the walls to reflect the view of the river into your apartment. This is extremely auspicious for wealth luck.

Finally, if none of these options is available to you, go and look for a really beautiful print or painting of a water scene – a rippling brook or a clean–flowing river – and then place it in the southeast. This is highly effective.

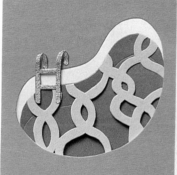

SWIMMING POOLS

Swimming pools can prove to be a problem. Rectangular-shaped pools tend to be frowned on by feng shui Masters, who prefer pools to be kidney-shaped. Let the pool seem to embrace the house and make sure it is not so large that it overwhelms the house. Pools should also be in the southeast, east, or north of your land. Anywhere else, and the large body of water could hurt rather than help the feng shui of the house.

JADE BELT WATER

Here water wraps around the house like a jade belt. The range of protective mountains behind the house represent the celestial turtle, the dragon and tiger hills are on either side, and the phoenix footstool is in front. Residents of a house with this configuration of water will enjoy great wealth, no matter how humble their beginnings.

THREE DIRECTION WATER

When water comes into view from three different directions and then collects in front of the house, the feng shui is described as extremely auspicious. In this case, it is bringing tremendous wealth luck to the residents that will stay intact within the family for many generations.

AUSPICIOUS WATER FLOW

There are three types of natural water flow that are said to be extremely auspicious. If your home faces, or is within the vicinity of such a flow, you will have great wealth luck for several generations. These are known as the three feeling waters – shown here for easy reference.

BROADENING WATER

This describes water that flows into view in a very broad expanse, then settles gently in front of the house's main entrance, before flowing away in a narrow ribbon and tapering out of sight. This is good feng shui water and wealth is said to have been brought with it and entered the home.

PROSPERITY NUMBERS AND GOOD-FORTUNE SYMBOLS

SIGNIFICANCE OF NUMBERS IN FENG SHUI

In addition to the elements, numbers are highly significant to the practice of feng shui. In this context, it is important to understand that feng shui numerology bears little resemblance to the various theories held by other cultures.

THE LO SHU SQUARE

Feng shui numerology has its roots in the arrangement of numbers around the Lo Shu magic square. The numbers one to nine are arranged in a nine-sector grid so that the sum of any three in a row – vertically, horizontally, or diagonally – is 15, the number of days of the lunar cycle from new to full moon. None of the numbers is regarded as lucky or unlucky in itself. Their significance becomes potent when they are combined with each other or when they are used in the application of various formulas.

The Lo Shu square is a very important symbol in feng shui practice, particularly in the use of advanced compass school formulas. Its arrangement of numbers is particularly significant when considering the time dimension in feng shui because the square can be used to calculate the luck of different parts and corners of a home from month to month, based on a method that is called flying star feng shui. This is practiced in Hong Kong. To activate wealth luck, however, we need to address the space aspect of feng shui.

The numbers in the Lo Shu square are arranged so that the sum of any row of three is 15.

AUSPICIOUS NUMBERS

Lo Shu feng shui also suggests that the following numbers are lucky.

The number seven is said to represent current prosperity up to the year 2003.

The number eight is said to signify future prosperity and is auspicious for business.

The number nine represents distant prosperity for the next generation.

Combinations of one, six, and eight are excellent prosperity numbers.

INAUSPICIOUS NUMBERS

Lo Shu feng shui also suggests the inauspicious combinations of numbers are as follows.

The numbers two and three together indicate quarrels and being stabbed in the back.

The numbers five and two together bring illness and diseases and indicate being robbed.

The double five means severe loss.

The double two means getting burgled.

Each sector of the Pa Kua and, therefore, each of the eight corners, as well as the center, is said to represent one of the numbers found in the Lo Shu square. The relationship is obtained by superimposing the Lo Shu square onto the Pa Kua and then onto the layout plan of the home itself, with the direction south at the top.

Despite this placement, magnetic north is still north. Using this method, you will see that the number of the southeast is said to be four, so placing things in groups of four in the southeast enhances the luck of this number in that corner. The number four is also said to be the Kua number of the southeast.

USING NUMBERS FOR GOOD LUCK

The Chinese have another theory about lucky and unlucky numbers. They base the luck of numbers on the way they sound phonetically. Thus they attribute certain qualities to certain numbers.

- ▓ Four is said to be extremely unlucky because it sounds like death.
- ▓ Eight is said to be fortunate because it sounds like growth with prosperity.
- ▓ Three is a good number because it also means growth.
- ▓ Two is lucky because it literally means easy to do.

Lo Shu feng shui places four as the Kua number of the wealth sector, so I regard it as an auspicious number. However, old beliefs die hard, especially among the Hokkiens and Cantonese dialect groups, who insist that four means death and so is bad. You must decide.

THE NUMBER NINE

Nine is said to be enormously auspicious because it represents the fullness of heaven and earth. Nine multiplied by any other number and then reduced to a single digit always adds up to nine. Thus **9x3=27** and **2+7=9**. Do this exercise in any combination and you will always come back to the single digit nine.

Businessmen in Asia love number plates with multiple nines, eights, and threes. They also use lucky numbers for their addresses, telephone numbers, and bank account numbers.

Choose an auspicious number for your car. Anything that ends with a nine or eight is usually lucky. Businessmen in Hong Kong often bid for auspicious car number plates. The highest sum paid was five million dollars when a local tycoon successfully bid for the single number 8. Other lucky numbers are 9999, 128, 148, 168, 7788, and 2188. Avoid a number plate ending in 58 or with a four.

Another number most Chinese consider very important is the house or apartment number. An auspicious address adds to your luck. It is considered taboo to have a four in the address, although I know of two people who became extremely rich and successful despite having a four and double four in their addresses.

Your personal and business communication numbers should be as auspicious as possible. Follow the general guidelines above. Try to use the eights and nines.

The number of your house is very important. Chinese prefer to avoid the number four in their addresses.

Did John Paul Getty use auspicious numbers to gain such immense success in business?

SYMBOLS OF PROSPERITY

There is a great deal of symbolism in the practice of feng shui. Central to this is the belief that displaying auspicious objects around the home attracts good-luck energies, especially when they are correctly displayed and placed in the right corners of the home. Thus, prosperity symbols should abound, since they represent money in various forms, particularly what passed as money in the past.

Fake gold and silver ingots made in the traditional boat shape are very popular, especially during the lunar New Year when they are freely displayed in the home. The fact that such pretend gold belongs to the metal element does not stop it from being placed near the main entrance, irrespective of the compass location of the front door.

The Chinese display fake gold ingots during their New Year celebrations to bring good luck.

ANCIENT CHINESE COINS

Probably the most popular symbols, however, are old Chinese coins with a square hole in the center. These coins have tremendous potency, especially when they are energized with red thread. There are many ways of using this particular good-fortune symbol.

USING COINS

Hang the coins, tied together with red thread, as mobiles in the southeast corner of the home. Do not overdo this. Three coins are sufficient.

Bury nine of these coins in a pathway just under the pavement that leads to your home, or if you live in an apartment, stick them under a mat just outside your door. This represents money making its way to your doorstep. Make sure red thread has been tied round the coins. If you run a retail store, this will greatly increase your sales and your turnover.

Tape three coins tied with red thread on the southeast corner of your work table or desk to energize money luck.

Place coins under paving stones and let the pathway curve. This is excellent prosperity feng shui.

Another excellent way of using the coins is to tie three coins together with red thread and then stick them onto your sales invoice files, check book, or any folder that has to do with your income. The coins are said to be powerful activators when used this way. Turnover increases and your income will receive healthy doses of unexpected good luck.

Tie three Chinese coins with red thread and attach them to your ledger book. The side with four characters on it should be facing up.

ADDITIONAL WAYS OF ACTIVATING MONEY LUCK

It is not uncommon to find Chinese coins, tied with red thread in various shapes, hung in offices behind the desk. Doing this activates the income generating potential of the coins and if you visit a Chinese emporium anywhere in the world, you will find them readily available.

THE THREE-LEGGED FROG

The three-legged frog with a coin in its mouth and surrounded by yet more coins signifies an abundance of riches. A frog is already a good-fortune symbol, but the three-legged frog is believed to symbolize something quite special. These frogs are not difficult to purchase in Chinese emporiums since they are widely used by the Chinese people in Hong Kong.

If you do find one and wish to display it in the home, the best place is on a low table in the living room in full view of the main door. Do not place the frog on the floor. It is always advisable to elevate good-fortune symbols slightly.

The frog is a symbol of good fortune to the Chinese. Display it in your home to enhance family wealth.

MONEY BAGS AND RED PACKETS

Placing a mock money bag or a red packet (lai see in Chinese) containing a $10 note in the rice urn is supposed to enhance the family wealth. The Chinese renew the red packet at the start of each lunar New Year. This ensures that the rice urn is always full, signifying that the family will always have plenty to eat. In the West, where rice is not the staple food, placing the money bag inside the bread bin could well be a practical substitute to ensure good fortune.

The rice urn is very symbolic to the Chinese. It represents the family's material well-being, and placing a red packet deep inside the urn ensures the family will never be lacking in food and prosperity.

INDIVIDUAL WEALTH ORIENTATIONS

THE COMPASS FORMULA

Your wealth direction, based on your date of birth, can be calculated using a potent compass feng shui formula that was a closely guarded secret for many years. It is derived from the two principal symbols of feng shui – the eight-sided Pa Kua, with its layers of meanings, and the Lo Shu magic square, a nine-sector grid that further unlocks the secrets of the ancient Pa Kua.

Also known as the Pa Kua Lo Shu formula (Kua formula for short), this method of investigating personal prosperity orientations was given to the author's feng shui Master by an old Taiwan feng shui Grand Master who was a legend in his time. As the personal consultant of many of Taiwan's richest men of the time, Master Chan Chuan Huay was an expert on wealth feng shui and was particularly well schooled in the science of water feng shui. He was also in possession of this Kua formula and used it with spectacular success for his clients, many of whom founded huge business conglomerates

that are managed today by their heirs and descendants. It is no coincidence that the small island of Taiwan is so rich. Feng shui has always been widely practiced there.

If your Kua number is:

1 east group

2 west group

3 east group

4 east group

5 west group

6 west group

7 west group

8 west group

9 east group

THE KUA FORMULA

To determine your wealth orientation, first determine your Kua number. Obtain your Chinese year of birth based on the calendar on pages 34-35 and use the following calculation to get your Kua number. There is no number 5 in this formula, although for clarity it is given below. Males with Kua number 5 should use number 2 instead, and females should use Kua number 8.

5+9=14
5
1959

Your wealth orientation is:

SOUTHEAST for both males and females

NORTHEAST for both males and females

SOUTH for both males and females

NORTH for both males and females

NORTHEAST for males and
SOUTHWEST for females

WEST for both males and females

NORTHWEST for both males and females

SOUTHWEST for both males and females

EAST for both males and females

THE KUA FORMULA

Calculate your Kua number as follows.
Add the last two digits of your Chinese
year of birth. e.g. **1967**, **6+7=13**.
If the sum is higher than ten, reduce to
a single digit, thus **1+3=4**.

Males	Females
Subtract from	Add
10	**5**
thus	thus
10-4	**5+4**
=6	**=9**
So, for men born in	So, for women born in
1967	**1967**
the Kua number is	the Kua number is
6	**9**

Now check against this table for your
family direction and location.

THE CHINESE CALENDAR

Note that the Chinese New Year begins in either late January or early February. When calculating your Kua number take note of this. Thus, if you were born in January 1946 before the New Year, your Chinese year of birth is said to be 1945 not 1946. This calendar also indicates the ruling element of your year of birth. This gives you further clues on which corner of the home will have the most effect on your well-being.

Year	From	To	Element	Year	From	To	Element
1900	31 Jan 1900	18 Feb 1901	Metal	1923	16 Feb 1923	4 Feb 1924	Water
1901	19 Feb 1901	17 Feb 1902	Metal	1924	5 Feb 1924	24 Jan 1925	Wood
1902	18 Feb 1902	28 Jan 1903	Water	1925	25 Jan 1925	12 Feb 1926	Wood
1903	29 Jan 1903	15 Jan 1904	Water	1926	13 Feb 1926	1 Feb 1927	Fire
1904	16 Feb 1904	3 Feb 1905	Wood	1927	2 Feb 1927	22 Jan 1928	Fire
1905	4 Feb 1905	24 Jan1906	Wood	1928	23 Jan 1928	9 Feb 1929	Earth
1906	25 Jan 1906	12 Feb 1907	Fire	1929	10 Feb 1929	29 Jan 1930	Earth
1907	13 Feb 1907	1 Feb 1908	Fire	1930	30 Jan 1930	16 Feb 1931	Metal
1908	2 Feb 1908	21 Jan 1909	Earth	1931	17 Feb 1931	15 Feb 1932	Metal
1909	22 Jan 1909	9 Feb 1910	Earth	1932	16 Feb 1932	25 Jan 1933	Water
1910	10 Feb 1910	29 Jan 1911	Metal	1933	26 Jan 1933	13 Feb 1934	Water
1911	30 Jan 1911	17 Feb 1912	Metal	1934	14 Feb 1934	3 Feb 1935	Wood
1912	18 Feb 1912	25 Feb 1913	Water	1935	4 Feb 1935	23 Jan 1936	Wood
1913	26 Feb 1913	25 Jan 1914	Water	1936	24 Jan 1936	10 Feb 1937	Fire
1914	26 Jan 1914	13 Feb 1915	Wood	1937	11 Feb 1937	30 Jan 1938	Fire
1915	14 Feb 1915	2 Feb 1916	Wood	1938	31 Jan 1938	18 Feb 1939	Earth
1916	3 Feb 1916	22 Jan 1917	Fire	1939	19 Feb 1939	7 Feb 1940	Earth
1917	23 Jan 1917	10 Feb 1918	Fire	1940	8 Feb 1940	26 Jan 1941	Metal
1918	11 Feb 1918	31 Jan 1919	Earth	1941	27 Jan 1941	14 Feb 1942	Metal
1919	1 Feb 1919	19 Feb 1920	Earth	1942	15 Feb 1942	24 Feb 1943	Water
1920	20 Feb 1920	7 Feb 1921	Metal	1943	25 Feb 1943	24 Jan 1944	Water
1921	8 Feb 1921	27 Jan 1922	Metal	1944	25 Jan 1944	12 Feb 1945	Wood
1922	28 Jan 1922	15 Feb 1923	Water	1945	13 Feb 1945	1 Feb 1946	Wood

Year	From	To	Element	Year	From	To	Element
1946	2 Feb 1946	21 Jan 1947	Fire	1977	18 Feb 1977	6 Feb 1978	Fire
1947	22 Jan 1947	9 Feb 1948	Fire	1978	7 Feb 1978	27 Jan 1979	Earth
1948	10 Feb 1948	28 Jan 1949	Earth	1979	28 Jan 1979	15 Feb 1980	Earth
1949	29 Jan 1949	16 Feb 1950	Earth	1980	16 Feb 1980	4 Feb 1981	Metal
1950	17 Feb 1950	5 Feb 1951	Metal	1981	5 Feb 1981	24 Jan 1982	Metal
1951	6 Feb 1951	26 Jan 1952	Metal	1982	25 Jan 1982	12 Feb 1983	Water
1952	27 Jan 1952	13 Feb 1953	Water	1983	13 Feb 1983	1 Feb 1984	Water
1953	14 Feb 1953	2 Feb 1954	Water	1984	2 Feb 1984	19 Feb 1985	Wood
1954	3 Feb 1954	23 Jan 1955	Wood	1985	20 Feb 1985	8 Feb 1986	Wood
1955	24 Jan 1955	11 Feb 1956	Wood	1986	9 Feb 1986	28 Jan 1987	Fire
1956	12 Feb 1956	30 Jan 1957	Fire	1987	29 Jan 1987	16 Feb 1988	Fire
1957	31 Jan 1957	17 Feb 1958	Fire	1988	17 Feb 1988	5 Feb 1989	Earth
1958	18 Feb 1958	7 Feb 1959	Earth	1989	6 Feb 1989	26 Jan 1990	Earth
1959	8 Feb 1959	27 Jan 1960	Earth	1990	27 Jan 1990	14 Feb 1991	Metal
1960	28 Jan 1960	14 Feb 1961	Metal	1991	15 Feb 1991	3 Feb 1992	Metal
1961	15 Feb 1961	4 Feb 1962	Metal	1992	4 Feb 1992	22 Jan 1993	Water
1962	5 Feb 1962	24 Jan 1963	Water	1993	23 Jan 1993	9 Feb 1994	Water
1963	25 Jan 1963	12 Feb 1964	Water	1994	10 Feb 1994	30 Jan 1995	Wood
1964	13 Feb 1964	1 Feb 1965	Wood	1995	31 Jan 1995	18 Feb 1996	Wood
1965	2 Feb 1965	20 Jan 1966	Wood	1996	19 Feb 1996	7 Feb 1997	Fire
1966	21 Jan 1966	8 Feb 1967	Fire	1997	8 Feb 1997	27 Jan 1998	Fire
1967	9 Feb 1967	29 Jan 1968	Fire	1998	28 Jan 1998	15 Feb 1999	Earth
1968	30 Jan 1968	16 Feb 1969	Earth	1999	16 Feb 1999	4 Feb 2000	Earth
1969	17 Feb 1969	5 Feb 1970	Earth	2000	5 Feb 2000	23 Jan 2001	Metal
1970	6 Feb 1970	26 Jan 1971	Metal	2001	24 Jan 2001	11 Feb 2002	Metal
1971	27 Jan 1971	15 Feb 1972	Metal	2002	12 Feb 2002	31 Jan 2003	Water
1972	16 Feb 1972	22 Feb 1973	Water	2003	1 Feb 2003	21 Jan 2004	Water
1973	23 Feb 1973	22 Jan 1974	Water	2004	22 Jan 2004	8 Feb 2005	Wood
1974	23 Jan 1974	10 Feb 1975	Wood	2005	9 Feb 2005	28 Jan 2006	Wood
1975	11 Feb 1975	30 Jan 1976	Wood	2006	29 Jan 2006	17 Feb 2007	Fire
1976	31 Jan 1976	17 Feb 1977	Fire	2007	18 Feb 2007	6 Feb 2008	Fire

APPLYING
THE KUA FORMULA IN THE HOME

Once you know your wealth direction, there are several ways you can match your own energies with that of your surroundings. You can activate positive energy or chi to your advantage. Your Kua number gives you your most auspicious direction. It also identifies your luckiest compass location and your luckiest Lo Shu number. The luck referred to here is money and success luck. When you activate your individual wealth direction and location, you are effectively enhancing your personal money and success luck.

HOW TO DO IT

The home layout should be demarcated into nine sectors according to the Lo Shu grid, as shown. To do this accurately, use a good compass (any Western compass will do) and, standing in the center of the home, identify the locations and divide the total floor space of the home into nine equal grids.

Make sure your main door faces your wealth direction.

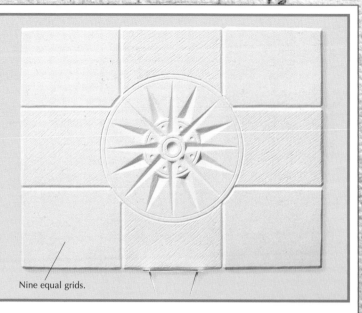

Nine equal grids.

THE MAIN DOOR

Try to locate your main door in your wealth location and try to let it face your wealth direction. If your wealth direction is south, the diagram here shows where and in what direction your main door should be facing.

The direction of your main door should face your wealth direction to activate your money and success luck.

IRREGULAR-SHAPED HOMES

Homes, apartments, and offices rarely have regular, square, or rectangular shapes, making it difficult to superimpose a nine-sector grid on to the layout. More serious is the problem of missing corners. There are ways of getting round this and some common problems and their solutions are shown here.

The example shown is a room with an irregular layout shape. By taking directions from the center, it is possible to see immediately which compass sector(s) are missing. According to feng shui, missing corners mean the home will be lacking in certain luck aspects. What type of luck is missing depends on the corresponding compass direction of the missing sector. If one missing sector represents your wealth direction, you can partially correct the matter in one of the following ways.

▨ Install a light.
▨ Hang a mirror on the wall.
▨ Build an extension.

What you do depends on your circumstances and whether you have the necessary available space.

Irregular-shaped layouts sometimes make it difficult to have the main door located or oriented in the most auspicious way. If you cannot activate the location, tapping the wealth direction alone is often good enough. If you cannot tap either the location or direction, try, at least, to have your main door face one of your four auspicious directions. Remember that directions are taken from inside the home facing outward.

Irregular-shaped rooms will have missing corners, which means that certain luck aspects will absent. Rectify this by installing a light or mirror in the room, or if you have space, build an extension.

SLEEPING, DINING, AND COOKING FOR WEALTH

Once you know your wealth direction, you can begin to activate it to enhance your income, by arranging your bed, sitting and cooking orientations within the home. It is by activating and using these personalized directions that feng shui becomes most potent.

THE OVEN 'MOUTH'

How your food is cooked also has a bearing on the quality of your luck. For the Chinese, whose staple food is rice, it is easy to orient the rice cooker so that its oven "mouth" is facing the wealth direction. The "mouth" is the place where the electricity enters the cooker, based on the hypotheses that the source of the energy that cooks the rice must come from the wealth direction, because it brings wealth (food) with it.

YOUR BED

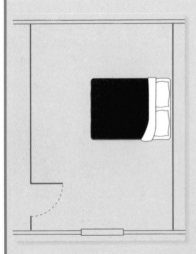

First make sure your bed is located in an auspicious way according to form school feng shui and then check that you are not sleeping under an overhead beam. You can then activate your wealth direction with your sleeping orientation.

The arrow shows you how to take the direction in the correct way. Note that the head must be pointed in the wealth direction. If you and your spouse have different wealth directions, either sleep in two separate beds or let the direction of the breadwinner prevail. Note also that the bed is placed diagonally to the door and the foot of the bed does not point to the door.

For Western homes, the orientation to get right is the source of energy to your oven or cooker This takes a bit of doing, but is worth it since getting the oven "mouth" correctly oriented is an important part of wealth feng shui.

YOUR DINING TABLE

Select the chair that allows you to sit facing your wealth direction. The arrows show you how to take the direction.

It is a good idea to place a full length mirror in the dining room to reflect the food on the table. This doubles the meal and is regarded as excellent wealth feng shui. Make sure the mirror is higher than the tallest person in the home.

PROTECTING THE MAIN DOOR

While you are activating your personalized wealth direction, you must also incorporate other important form school feng shui guidelines in your arrangements. These have nothing to do with the formula guidelines, but combine the rules of form school feng shui with compass feng shui specifications.

In the practice of feng shui, basic fundamentals must never be ignored. You can have every direction and orientation absolutely correct and yet be hit by what is termed killing breath, or shar chi. Killing breath is so harmful that it negates all the good feng shui you may have carefully arranged. It is caused by dominating structures in your immediate environment that seem to threaten your home. These so-called poison arrows are especially dangerous when your main entrance door is being hit directly by their killing breath. It is far better to get a less auspicious direction than to face your wealth direction and be struck by poison arrows of shar chi.

THINGS TO WATCH OUT FOR

Structures that can hurt your main door are present in the immediate external environment, as well as inside the home itself. Some common examples of harmful structures are shown here.

A triangular roof line from a neighboring house or building can cause shar chi.

If the door opens directly on to a staircase it is better to relocate or re-orient the door.

FROM THE OUTSIDE

A tall and threatening building located directly in front of your main door is bad feng shui.

A dead tree trunk is particularly dangerous and a single tree is also harmful.

ON THE INSIDE

If the door opens on to a toilet, the energy is very harmful. The toilet turns good luck chi into killing breath.

If the door directly faces a column, whether round or square, it blocks the good luck chi from entering the home. It is better to re-orient the door.

FENG SHUI FOR BUSINESS AND COMMERCE

生
意

THE RETAIL STORE

If you own a retail store, energizing wealth luck through feng shui depends on what sort of business you are in. Determine the element that best repre- sents the things you sell, and then acti- vate the relevant compass direction corner that symbolizes that element. Display objects and paintings, or decorate with motifs suggestive of the element. Some categories of businesses and their matching elements are shown here.

Activate **metal** (northwest and west) if you are in the jewelry or boutique business. Avoid using red, and place a windchime in the metal corners. Placing a crystal in the west is also auspicious.

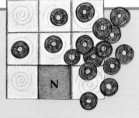

Activate **water** (north) if you are in any business that deals with money. Bank and insurance branches, bars, and even restaurants qualify as water enterprises. Place a water feature in the north and decorate your store with a water motif.

Activate **wood** (the east or southeast) if you run a grocery business or are engaged in selling things made of paper or wood. Place a plant in the east corner of your store.

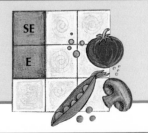

DECORATING IDEAS

Horseshoe-shaped magnets can be used to activate metal. Natural quartz or cut crystals are also very lucky.

The best and most beautiful way to energize wood is to make the fullest use of plants. Even artificial silk plants are acceptable. However, do not use dried plants or driftwood.

Use lights to activate fire or regularly light a candle in the south. Alternatively, decorate with the fire or sun motif. Effectively activating the fire element will give your store a great reputation.

One of the best ways of energizing the earth element for business is to display the globe – to develop export markets, twirl it daily

The water element can be energized by using water motifs or by installing a water feature, such as a small fountain or even a bowl of water. Remember that activating water is good for most businesses.

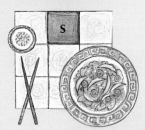

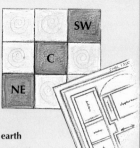

Activate **fire** (the south) if you are in the catering or restaurant business (cooking connotes fire), or if you are selling light fixtures. Install a bright light, kept on continuously, in the south and at the entrance. A jade plant or small aquarium at the entrance is also auspicious for the business.

Activate **earth** (southwest, northeast and center) if you are in real estate or if you are an architect or developer. Use earth colors for your decor and place natural quartz or faceted lead crystals in the earth sectors of your store or office.

DOUBLING YOUR TURNOVER –
TWO EXCELLENT TIPS

Protecting the cash register is vital. The cash register or credit card machine is the most important item in your store. It symbolizes your revenue and income. First, make sure nothing sharp or pointed is aimed at it: this can be the sharp edge of a protruding corner, an overhead beam, open book shelves, or even a pointed object, such as a pair of scissors or a blade left idly by.

TIP ONE

Hang a windchime immediately above the cash register. Make sure the rods of the chime are hollow, as this is the feature that will encourage the chi to rise. The tinkling sounds of the chimes also encourage the creation of abundant good-fortune chi. There can be any number of rods on the windchime, except five which is inauspicious. If you cannot find a windchime, hang three Chinese coins tied with red thread.

A variation of this popular method is to hang tiny bells at the door. This not only announces a customer's entry, it also attracts good-fortune chi into the store.

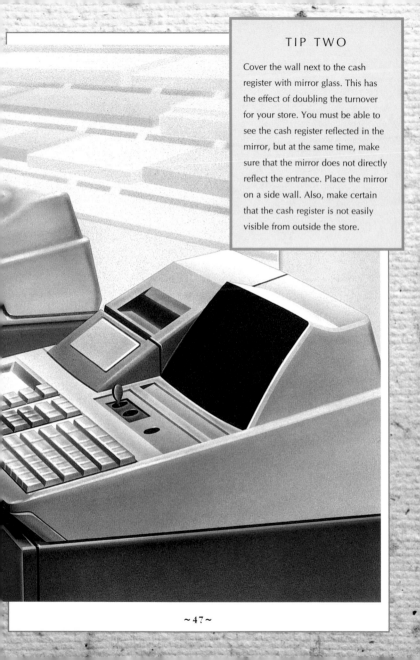

TIP TWO

Cover the wall next to the cash register with mirror glass. This has the effect of doubling the turnover for your store. You must be able to see the cash register reflected in the mirror, but at the same time, make sure that the mirror does not directly reflect the entrance. Place the mirror on a side wall. Also, make certain that the cash register is not easily visible from outside the store.

CORPORATE FENG SHUI

THE CORPORATE HEAD OFFICE

商業

Corporate feng shui always begins with protective measures to deflect or dissolve the effects of any killing chi caused by pointed or hostile structures aimed at the entrance of the head office. Protect the entrance doors, block off these hidden poison arrows, and, where necessary, retaliate with a strategically positioned Pa Kua mirror or even a cannon.

The cannon is a very powerful defensive tool in feng shui and should not be used lightly, since it causes extremely bad feng shui for any residence or office hit by it. However, when the offending structure is the edge of a massive building or other sharp arrow-like structure, you may have no choice but to use a cannon. If you do, make sure it is pointed directly only at the offending structure. Place it outside your building as a decorative object. Use an old cannon but if you cannot get your hands on a genuine one, a model will do just as well.

Use either a real cannon or a model of one to deflect the effects of killing chi.

TIPS FOR FINANCIAL SUCCESS

A Try to have a small plot of empty land, such as a playground or park, directly in front of the building. This empty space is termed the auspicious bright hall, where good-fortune chi can settle and accumulate before entering the building. If this is not possible, then at least make sure the entrance does not feel cramped or overwhelmed by the buildings surrounding it.

B Try to avoid being squeezed between two taller buildings. If you are, place a very bright light on the roof of your building and switch it on every day at nighttime.

C If a straight road approaches your building, re-orient the door so that the straight and pernicious energies of the road – like tigers in the night – cannot enter your building. If you can, place a wall of water, flowing inward toward the building, between the road and your entrance.

D If a new building is erected in front of your building, causing your company's fortunes to flounder, take remedial action immediately. Either re-orient your own building completely by changing the entrance direction or use the cannon. Alternatively, you can install plenty of lights and big fountains to attract chi toward your building, despite any blockages that it may experience.

E If there is a river flowing near your building, make every attempt to orient your front door to face it and get the compass direction to match with the flow of the water. If the river flows past the back rather than front door, you will miss every opportunity to grow, expand, and flourish.

F If there are escalators directly facing the entrance to your building, ensure that they move in a well-lit and landscaped atrium. Escalators leading to an open space force fast-moving, inauspicious energy to become gentle and auspicious. Otherwise, they can cause problems for the company.

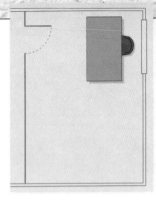

FENG SHUI IN THE OFFICE

Even if your offices are overcrowded, success will come by following some simple feng shui ground rules.

- ▓ Reception areas should be well lit. The receptionist should sit with her back to a wall blocking the general office from view of the entrance.
- ▓ Do not arrange desks in a confrontational manner – one directly facing the other. It is better if office colleagues sit side-by-side.
- ▓ Arrange the desks in such a way that there is a meandering flow in the traffic.
- ▓ Avoid having too many partitions that result in long corridors being created in the layout. This leads to quarrels, backbiting, and disharmony in the office.
- ▓ Do not station key personnel in rooms that are located at the end of a long corridor. If the finance director sits there, your company's finances will be affected. If the marketing director sits there, sales will be adversely affected.

BAD DESK PLACEMENT:

- ▓ The desk is too near the door
- ▓ The occupant sits with his or her back to the door
- ▓ The occupant is sitting with his or her back to a window.

GOOD DESK PLACEMENT:

- ▓ The desk is diagonal to the door
- ▓ The occupant is facing the door
- ▓ A solid wall is behind the occupant.

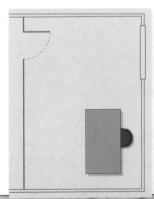

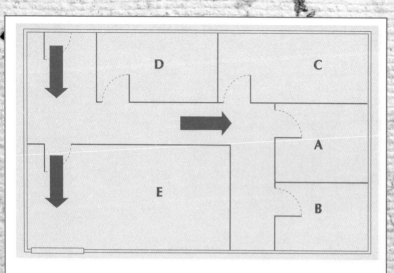

Follow feng shui rules to maximize success in the office environment.

The receptionist should sit with her back to the wall.

OFFICE PLACEMENT

A Is an inauspicious office location.

B Is the best as it is diagonal to the entrance.

C Is a good location for the boardroom.

D Is too near the door.

E Shows two doors in a row with a window in the general office. This could not be worse.

GOOD RECEPTION AREA.

Chi is forced to meander upon entering the office. The receptionist is sitting with the solid support provided by the wall.

THE CHIEF EXECUTIVE'S OFFICE

▧ Destroy any poison arrows by eliminating protruding corners, free-standing pillars, open book shelves, and overhead beams.

▧ Activate the wealth corner of the office with a healthy and vibrant plant in the southeast.

▧ Arrange the office so that the chief executive can sit facing his or her wealth direction (check the Kua number). What is good for the chief executive is good for the company.

▧ Keep the office well lit. Place a light in the south corner to ensure success in all executive decisions.

▧ Place a painting of a mountain behind the chief executive to ensure that he or she has support at all times.

THE BOARDROOM

The feng shui of the boardroom is important for a company's fortunes simply because major decisions are taken there. The success of the company can be adversely affected if there is killing breath present in this room, either caused by protruding corners or because windows open to offensive structures that allow shar chi to enter.

Check the chairperson's seating placement. This should preferably be away from the entrance, with his or her back properly supported by a solid wall.

Do not have too many doors opening into the boardroom, as this leads to quarrels and misunderstandings, and is not conducive to the generation of wealth.

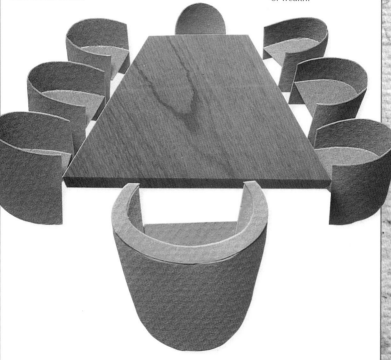

Let each member of the board sit in his or her wealth direction. This enhances the feng shui of the company.

USING COINS IN WEALTH FENG SHUI

Coins have always been a popular symbol of prosperity in ancient China and using old and antique coins as amulets and for feng shui purposes is very widespread. This is especially so among the business community.

These coins are round with a square hole in the center. The circle is representative of heaven, while the square symbolizes earth. In human hands, the coin represents the trinity of luck.

Tied with auspicious red thread, the coin is regarded as a very potent symbol for attracting excellent business and wealth luck. The Chinese believe that when these antique coins are sewn onto tunics they bring auspicious luck to the person who wears them.

COIN TIPS FOR ACTIVATING WEALTH LUCK

Hang ten antique coins tied together with red thread over a door to attract wealth to the establishment. Coins are always activated with red thread. Always use red thread to breath energy into these prosperity symbols.

If you are displaying the god of wealth in your home or office, tie three coins with red thread around his neck. This is believed to attract wonderful financial opportunities.

Design a driveway toward the main door in a formation of coins. This symbolizes a flow of wealth coming toward your door. Some Masters advocate burying ten old coins under the driveway.

Hang objects that are completely covered with coins and tied together with red thread, behind your desk at work. This will ensure financial success for your project.

INDEX

FURTHER READING

Kwok, Man-Ho and O'Brien, Joanne,
The Elements of Feng Shui,
ELEMENT BOOKS, SHAFTESBURY, 1991

Lo, Raymond *Feng Shui: The Pillars of
Destiny (Understanding Your Fate and
Fortune),* TIMES EDITIONS, SINGAPORE, 1995

Skinner, Stephen, *Living Earth Manual
of Feng Shui: Chinese Geomancy,*
PENGUIN, 1989

Too, Lillian, *The Complete Illustrated
Guide to Feng Shui,* ELEMENT BOOKS,
SHAFTESBURY, 1996

Too, Lillian, *Basic Feng Shui,*
KONSEP BOOKS, KUALA LUMPAR, 1997

Too, Lillian, *Chinese Astrology for Romance
and Relationships,* KONSEP BOOKS,
KUALA LUMPAR, 1996

Too, Lillian *Chinese Numerology
in Feng Shui,* KONSEP BOOKS,
KUALA LUMPUR, 1994

Too, Lillian, *Dargon Magic,*
KONSEP BOOKS, KUALA LUMPAR, 1996

Too, Lillian *Feng Shui,* KONSEP BOOKS,
KUALA LUMPUR, 1993

Too, Lillian *Practical Applications for
Feng Shui,* KONSEP BOOKS, KUALA LUMPUR, 1994

Too, Lillian *Water Feng Shui for Wealth,*
KONSEP BOOKS, KUALA LUMPUR, 1995

Walters, Derek *Feng Shui Handbook:
A Practical Guide to Chinese Geomancy
and Environmental Harmony,*
AQUARIAN PRESS, 1991

USEFUL ADDRESSES

Feng Shui Design Studio
PO Box 705, Glebe, Sydney, NSW 2037,
Australia, Tel: 61 2 315 8258

Feng Shui Society of Australia
PO Box 1565, Rozelle, Sydney
NSW 2039, Australia

The Geomancer
The Feng Shui Store
PO Box 250, Woking, Surrey GU21 1YJ
Tel: 44 1483 839898
Fax: 44 1483 488998

Feng Shui Association
31 Woburn Place, Brighton BN1 9GA,
Tel/Fax: 44 1273 693844

Feng Shui Network International
PO Box 2133, London W1A 1RL,
Tel: 44 171 935 8935,
Fax: 44 171 935 9295

The School of Feng Shui
34 Banbury Road, Ettington,
Stratford-upon-Avon, Warwickshire
CV37 7SU. Tel/Fax: 44 1789 740116

The Feng Shui Institute of America
PO Box 488, Wabasso, FL 32970,
Tel: 1 407 589 9900 Fax: 1 407 589 1611

Feng Shui Warehouse
PO Box 3005, San Diego, CA 92163,
Tel: 1 800 399 1599 Fax: 1 800 997 9831

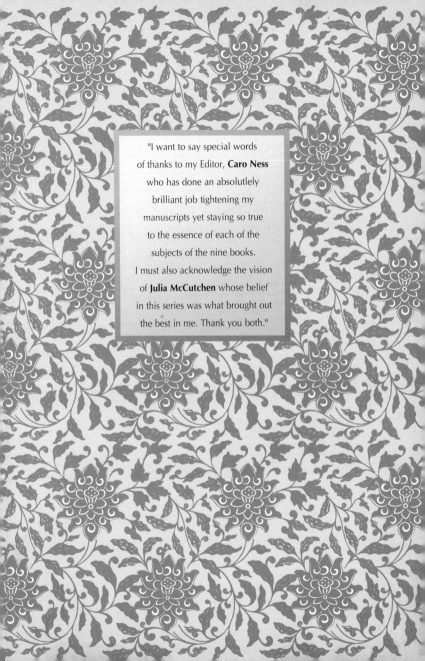

"I want to say special words of thanks to my Editor, **Caro Ness** who has done an absolutlely brilliant job tightening my manuscripts yet staying so true to the essence of each of the subjects of the nine books. I must also acknowledge the vision of **Julia McCutchen** whose belief in this series was what brought out the best in me. Thank you both."

make up fifty per cent of the undergraduates they were good at making their presence felt, giggling and shrieking in corridors, running about in noisy little groups carrying bags overflowing with books. Tampax boxes, hairbrushes and *billets-doux*.

The girls were very colourful, Leofred reflected, as he walked past. Most of them wore skimpy little ra-ra skirts in brilliant orange or fluorescent yellow, and dinky little pumps on their bare brown feet. He was too sunk in his self-deprecating gloom to really appreciate the spectacle, and marched past with his eyes fixed on the ground . . . until he heard a familiar voice and looked up into the face of Hilary Ardent.

Hilary was the college heart-throb. She had sharp, pointed little features and a curtain of spun-gold hair that seemed to be continually swishing to and fro. In theory, Leofred despised her, yet every time he saw her he couldn't prevent a slight quickening of the pulse as she looked at him with her shrewd, foxy little eyes and ran her tongue over her lower lip in a calculating manner. He was as much a victim as any of the other men around her.

Leofred immediately recognised the crowd that Hilary was with. It would have been difficult not to. They were the faces regularly adorning a column called *The Beautiful People* which appeared in the university newspaper, *CAMSHAFT*. *The Beautiful People* was a gossip column of sorts, reporting on the drunken parties attended, and the partner-swapping indulged in, by a small clique of people who were all friends of, or had slept with, *CAMSHAFT*'s editor. Few people ever read the column apart from the people who were in it, and one or two nonentities who aspired to be in it, but it was difficult to ignore the photographs, those laughing, luminous faces that beaming out of it, revealing the benefits of private dental care.

Hilary Ardent caught Leofred's eye and gave him a smile,

that special smile that was reserved for nobodies, the one that demanded a smile in return, which would then be ignored. One of the girls in the crowd, Lana Gilroy, read English and knew Leofred slightly. She waved at him, anxious to prove to the others that she knew a lot of people around the college, especially people with unusual and Bohemian-sounding names like Leofred.

'Hi, Leofred!' she shouted. 'We're all going to the buttery, are you coming?'

The buttery was the college bar, an inappropriately pastoral name for a dank cellar whose floor was coated with a thin slime of brown ale and potato-crisp dandruff.

Leofred shrugged. 'I don't think so.' He went back to his bed. It was empty apart from the suitcase in the middle of the room and a few half-packed cardboard boxes of books. The message from the St Godbore administration was clear – at the end of Trinity term the rooms must be left exactly as the students found them.

They needn't have fears on that score, thought Leofred, looking round him at the open-weave polyester curtains in burnt orange, the drooping olive-drab anglepoise lamp, the chipboard desk and wardrobe. Their precious room was completely undefiled. No amorous love scenes had left sticky smears on the mock-Spanish tapestry bedspread (one hundred per cent nylon). The dull green walls had escaped the sort of party where jelly and ice cream were flung.

Leofred sat on the edge of the bed and stared at the piles of books. On the top of one was a copy of *P. J. WIMLEY, Structuralism; a raison d'être*. It was in the pile ear-marked for vacation reading. He picked it up and threw it in the box with the others, then changed his mind and flung it into the bin instead.

It was time to contemplate the summer. Leofred had planned to do a little desultory reading, spend a few weeks in London, sleeping on his sister's floor and saving up the wages of some temporary job, then go to the Continent and perhaps tour France for a couple of weeks before returning to St Godbore's. But after Wimley's pronouncements he could see that this plan would not do at all. It was a mediocre plan, a boring plan, a predictable plan. One which would render him unchanged by his three and a half months' freedom. He would have to revise his strategy. In order to seek inspiration, he set off to the buttery for a drink.

The Beautiful People were still there, and so was Hilary Ardent. She was standing on tip-toe and leaning over the bar, her bright mini-skirt riding up just high enough for everyone to know that she was wearing black lace knickers. She ignored Leofred as he bought his drink.

'Half a pint of – no, make that a treble vodka.' Feeling flushed with the thrill of non-conformity, he took his drink and sat down. Apart from Hilary's crowd, there was no-one in the buttery. He felt he would draw attention to himself if he sat in isolated splendour, nor did he wish to join them, so he compromised by choosing a seat that bordered on the group; half in it and half not.

Conversation centred on how the summer was to be spent.

'What about you, Justin?'

'Nothing too exciting. Going to a gypsy festival in the Camargue. Should be quite a laugh.'

'God, lucky you! I've got to work all summer. I've gone and got myself roped into a series of celebrity interviews for *Bizarre*.'

There were sympathetic cries of 'God, what a drag!' and 'Oh no, Posie, how awful!'

'Yeah, it's a real shame, actually, because it means that Posie won't be able to come with us. We're going ballooning over the Sahara.'

'But that's terrible! It means you won't be able to come to Crispin's party!'

'I know, and this year he's got this really brilliant idea. We're all flying over to Brazil and Crisp's holding a house-party on board this boat he's taking up the Amazon.'

Leofred choked on his vodka.

'What about you?' asked Hilary Ardent, strolling back from the bar.

There was a pointed silence. '*Me?*' gasped Leofred.

'Fancy going to a party on the Amazon?'

Leofred gaped. Hilary laughed and turned away and suddenly Leofred was invisible again. She hadn't been serious.

There were smothered giggles from the corner. ' . . . '*Course he can't come!*' The voices were lowered ostentatiously. '*Look at him! . . . Probably going to Hollywood to star in a movie!*'

More snorts of laughter.

Leofred stood up and stumbled from the bar, feeling as though the vodka had left a window wide open in his brain.

But he was smiling. Why shouldn't I? he thought, the very possibility making him omnipotent. Why shouldn't I? In fact it's a very good idea. That's exactly what I should do this summer, to make the Peter Wimleys and Hilary Ardents of this world sit up and take notice.

I should go to Hollywood.

In North West London there is a no-man's land that is not quite Kilburn and not quite Queen's Park. The roads are so long that one can walk down them for nearly half an hour and not seem to get anywhere. The houses passed on the way are 1930s semis with grotesque gabling and stucco painted in unsuitable colours; apple green and damson.

One or two of them have what aspires to be a classical frieze of white plaster figures gambolling across their suburban elevation.

One such street is Grafton Road. Twenty-four-year-old Heidi Plunkett was walking along it, kicking cans. There weren't actually many cans to kick, only a Low-Alcohol Lager Party Pak, but that was the sort of mood she was in. She had had a frustrating day at work, she was hot and cross.

Heidi walked along this road twice a day, but she never failed to feel indignant at the length of time it took to get from the end of the road nearest the tube station to number two hundred and one, where she lived. The house was divided into bedsits and one studio flat which Heidi rented; a studio flat being a glorified bedsitter with a lavatory of its own, that cost twice as much to rent.

The payphone in the hall was ringing as Heidi came in, but she ignored it. No-one ever answered the phone downstairs, because when they did it always turned out to be a man with an indecipherable Middle Eastern accent asking for Mr Mohammed, who didn't live there anyway.

Heidi had an answering service. She didn't really need it, but since she worked in television and everyone else who worked in television had an answering service, Heidi had got one too, just in case she missed out on something. The red light was flashing. Heidi dropped her bag and hurried over to switch it on, hoping that Charles might have telephoned, but it was only someone trying to sell her double glazing.

'Christ, that's the last thing I want!' she muttered angrily, making her way over to the window and opening it to air the hot, stuffy room. This feat was by no means easy, since Heidi was an exceptionally disorganised person, and in order to cross the room she had to negotiate several tangled piles of clothes and remove sundry cups of cold tea from the windowsill. The sun had been beating down on the panes for about ten hours, giving the room the feel of a warmed-over meal. Leftovers.

Heidi stripped down to a T-shirt and knickers, pulled a can of Budweiser out of the fridge and flung herself into the armchair, drinking greedily. She belched with satisfaction, reaching out to switch on the TV with her big toe.

'. . . *And later on this evening, agony auntie Rachel Ryman will be here to tell you ladies out there how to get your man . . .*'

Jesus, if only someone could, thought Heidi. She pictured her lover, Charles Jolyon, one of the directors of the independent television network, TV Mayhem. She pictured their first lunch together when he had reached across the table to hold her hand and look at her with those soulful brown eyes.

'My wife just doesn't understand me, Heidi . . . our marriage is a disaster.'

'Why don't you leave her then?' Heidi had asked unsympathetically, breaking off a piece of bread roll and cramming it into her mouth. She went on with her mouth full, 'It sounds as though you should.'

Charles gave a pained smile and touched her hand again. 'Heidi . . . how young you are! Don't lose that wonderful naïveté, will you? . . . If only it were that simple though, little Heidi. The children . . . it would crucify them. And then there's Joy. I dread to think what it would do to her. She's so utterly dependent on me . . . oh!' He ran his hand through his luxuriant curls with a world-weary gesture. 'You've no idea what a burden it is having someone depend on you so.'

Heidi had shrugged and continued to munch on her bread roll, massaging his crotch with her bare foot under the table. Charles seemed to be comforted by this, and cast off the burden of his responsibilities long enough to find a hotel room for the afternoon.

Heidi groaned with pleasure at the memory. God, she adored him, Charles Jolyon, with his wounded-looking eyes and long tapering fingers. If only . . .

' . . . *So, girls,*' the agony aunt was saying, '*if the man you've picked is the right man for you, you need only snap your fingers and he'll come running –* '

'BOLLOCKS!' shouted Heidi, taking another swig of beer. She switched channels with her foot.

' . . . *interview with Mr Ivo Cathcart, Britain's youngest billionaire. As you all know, Ivo Cathcart is the founder of Rapier Industries, a marketing and leisure multi-conglomerate that turned over 2.5 billion last year. You'll all be familiar with the Rapier cinemas and supermarkets, and soon we'll be able to jet across the world on Rapier jets. So, Mr Cathcart – by the way, I understand your wife has just given birth again: congratulations –* '

'PISS OFF!' screamed Heidi. Christ, you couldn't get away from the bloody man; whenever you switched on the television or opened a newspaper there he was, grinning smugly. He was an exceptionally ugly man, short and squat with a round, red face, little eyes recessed in his face like two currants and a nose that bore a strong resemblance to a pig's snout. Heidi couldn't stand the sight of him.

She flicked to the next channel.

'*It's Friday! It's eight-forty-five and it's time for our super quiz game How Well Do You Know Your Dog?! On tonight's show we have Mrs Perkins from Gwent with her pet chow, Geoff Boycott. Now, that's an unusual name, Mrs Perkins –* !'
. . . *God, I don't believe it, it's one of mine!*

Heidi's job at TV Mayhem required her to dream up new ideas for television shows, for which she was paid a pitiful salary and given the title 'Assistant to the Assistant New Programme Development Manager', plus free vouchers for the subsidised canteen where she had the privilege of rubbing shoulders with the stars of breakfast television. In reality she was something of a Girl Friday, being put to work wherever she was needed. Heidi switched off the set and wandered over to the window, crumpling the beer can with her hand and tossing it in the direction of the bin. Outside in Grafton Road, the sun was sinking low in the sky, striping the pavements with the long, thin shadows of lamp-posts. Two pigeons on the roof began copulating clumsily. Heidi groaned. She thought about Charles, wondered whether he was having dinner with Joy and, if so, what they were talking about.

Speculation quickly became unbearable as she set about tidying the room instead. Pieces of furniture emerged from under the layer of clothes and eventually the carpet could be seen, though it was such an unpleasant shade of brown that it would have been better off covered. The walls were light purple and there was a pair of instant curtains to match, the sort that are bought in a chain store ready to hang. Heidi picked up a piece of paper and started to crumple it, then recognised it as an invitation to the wedding of her best friend. '*Mr and Mrs David Pearce request the pleasure of your company at the marriage of their daughter Josephine Anne to Mr Michael Glasing, on Monday July 1st . . .* ' She propped it on the mantelpiece.

The telephone rang and Heidi leapt from one corner of the room to another, trying to find it. Tidying the room had made it disappear. She eventually found it under the bed with her old eyeless teddybear, and snatched up the receiver with a trembling hand. It was probably Charles. He had managed to sneak away from the house for five minutes in order to ring her.

'BEEP-BEEP-BEEP.'

At the sound of a call box, Heidi's heart leapt and her pulse raced in Pavlovian response. But the voice on the other end of the line was quite incomprehensible.

' . . . No, Mr Mohammed does *not* live here – '

She slammed the phone down, but it rang again. 'I said . . . what? . . . Oh my God, Leofred, it's you! I didn't recognise your voice . . . you sound rather, er, drunk . . . what? You need to buy a ticket to Los Angeles? What on earth for? So you're coming to London tomorrow. Hang on – ' Heidi groped for her red PVC Organofax. 'Look, let's meet for lunch and we can talk about it then. Okay? . . . let's say . . .'

She came up with the only place she could think of, a trendy restaurant near the TV Mayhem headquarters where Charles sometimes took important contacts. He never took *her* there in case people from work saw them together.

' . . . meet me at the Basmati Brasserie at one o'clock.'

'BEEP-BEEP-BEEP.'

Heidi put the phone down, disgruntled. She didn't even know whether Leofred had heard her. And what if Charles had been trying to get through? She stared at the telephone. *Ring, damn you, ring!* Silence. Tentatively, she lifted the receiver.

Oh, what was the use! She slammed it down again and pressed the 'Record' button on her answering machine.

'Hello, this is Heidi Plunkett and I'm afraid I can't be bothered to answer the phone at the moment, so you'll just have to stuff it.'

Then she switched off the light, flung herself on the bed and buried herself beneath her duvet.

A few hours later, while Heidi slept, Jay Cathcart was grooving the night away at the Bao-Wow club in Soho. He sashayed across the floor to Sade, giving his male friends a brief squeeze on the shoulder when he passed them, raising an eyebrow at the girls he knew. It was not always easy to spot them since they were all dressed in black, camouflaged in the subterranean gloom of the place. Only their enormous earrings shone out like beacons, catching the disco light as they moved. Their dancing seemed to be governed by a policy of economy; they covered as little ground as possible, employing only a sexy shrug of the shoulders and a nonchalant swaying of their arms as they trod on the spot. Anyone who thrashed their limbs around wildly earned themselves a pitying smile from these sirens. *Definitely* uncool.

It was just as well that no-one exerted themselves on the dance floor, as the Bao-Wow Club was tiny, a former pornoflick studio on the first floor of a narrow old building, above an artificial-limb supplier. Entry was for members only, and the criteria for eligibility never fully explained to those who were turned away.

Jay cruised over to the bar. The barman, who had been to the same school, recognised him.

'Hey! Jay, my man!' They slapped palms.

'*Que pasa, pero?*' enquired Jay.

'Good, pretty good, how about you?'

But Jay had already moved on. He drifted towards the DJ. 'Hey, have you got the new one by . . . what's their name? . . .'

'Sixties and soul music only,' said the DJ coldly. 'Or rock'n'roll.'

'Quite right, quite right,' agreed Jay. 'Don't want any of that naffo seventies disco crap!'

He checked his Rolex. Three o'clock. He was bored. Time to round up the people he'd promised a lift to.

'Cindi, Simon – come on, we're splitting.'

A pretty blonde girl dressed in black and a laconic young man slithered off the dance floor. They squeezed into the lift together, giggling a lot as they did so. It was the only way into and out of the club, and since it was really only big enough for two people, it had become a good way of getting to know fellow 'members'. On the ground floor a queue of people was waiting eagerly to penetrate the club. Five of them charged the lift and pulled the iron gate shut, disappearing from view head first as the cage cranked its way up the narrow shaft. When only their legs were still visible, there was a loud squeak.

'Torquil, get your hand from under my skirt!'

'My hands are in my pockets – look . . .'

Jay had parked his car with his usual flair in the middle of the pavement. 'Come on kids, jump in,' he said. 'We're going to cruise.'

They hit Piccadilly at a steady fifty-five with the roof down and the stereo blaring, jumping four red lights in succession.

'*I have prayed for America!*
I was made for America! . . .'

''Ere,' shouted a taxi driver as Jay whistled past his left wing. 'You plonker! You're well out of order, you are!'

'*It's in my blood and in my bones . . .*' they sang, laughing.

'Hey, I've got an idea,' said Jay. 'Let's go and call on my brother, wake him up!'

'Are you sure that's a good idea?' asked Cindi. 'Hasn't his wife just had a baby?'

'Oh, don't worry about that. He keeps Linda and the kids holed up at his place in the country.'

Jay yanked the steering wheel left, shot down St James's Street and turned into an elegant square of white Regency houses. He screeched to a halt outside one with a bright pink front door and jumped out, with the engine still running.

'*Hey, Ivo!*' he shouted. 'Wake up, you hear!'

'Perhaps he'd lend me a thousand quid' sniggered Cindi, 'My overdraft's in a terrible condition.'

'We'll ask him,' said Jay. '*Hey Ivo, you rich bastard! Gissa grand!*'

The others snorted with laughter.

'Come on, we'll just have to go and ask him.'

They followed Jay up the steps. He rang the doorbell.

A very superior-looking butler complete with white gloves answered the door. He looked at Jay's face, then slowly down to his sockless feet and up again.

'Sir?'

Jay gave a disbelieving laugh. 'Hey . . . c'mon. You know who I am! I'm Mr Cathcart's brother. I want you to tell him I've called round to see him.'

'One moment sir, I'll announce you.' Without moving a muscle of his face, the butler turned around and walked slowly and stiffly up the stairs.

Jay grinned at his friends, who were admiring the Holbeins and the Italian marble flooring. 'Nifty place, huh? Cost half a mill., seven years ago.' He picked up a solid jet lighter, tossed it in the air and caught it.

The butler came back.

'Mr Cathcart says, sir,' he intoned without altering his facial expression a fraction, 'that you are a no-good, drunken pain in the arse and he has no wish to entertain you or your companions. He wishes you goodnight.'

The pink door closed in their faces. Disgruntled, Jay drove to the nearest tube station and dropped off the others.

'But Jay!' squeaked Cindi. 'The tubes stopped hours ago!'

'You can still get a cab,' Jay replied, without sympathy.

And he turned round his Twin-Cam turbo-charged Intercooler and headed for home.

Two

The next day was Saturday. Jay Cathcart slept until noon. He then slid from beneath his steel-grey duvet and went into the kitchen. The fridge contained nothing but 35mm film, Perrier and tonic water. Cursing, Jay went to the phone and started ringing around to find someone to have lunch with.

In Grafton Road, Heidi was woken at seven by the telephone ringing. The answering machine clicked on, but Heidi leapt out of bed to intercept it.

'Darling, it's me.'

'Charles! Where are you?'

'I'm at work. Listen darling, are you coming in this morning?'

'Why?'

'*Why do you think?*' hissed Charles, and Heidi smiled to herself. 'Because I want to see you, that's why!'

'Well I'm supposed to be coming in to do G.Y.K.O.Y.H., so – '

In the background she could hear the noise of a door opening and closing. Charles suddenly adopted his company director's voice. 'Yes . . . right . . . fine. We'll talk later. Bye.'

The line went dead.

Heidi threw on a pair of baggy shorts and a T-shirt and set off along the endless length of Grafton Road to the tube station.

Her destination was the headquarters of TV Mayhem. This vast example of architectural apoplexy rose above the drab streets of Ladbroke Grove, its pink towers like twin cow's udders.

'Good-morning-can-I-help-you?' droned the receptionist, plying Heidi with a plastic smile.

'I work here!' said Heidi, stomping crossly towards the tubular glass staircase. The same thing happened to her every day. No-one ever knew who she was. The TV Mayhem personalities, whom everyone always recognised, smiled at her from their huge blown-up photographs as she passed by.

Heidi was headed for Studio Three, where a live programme was being recorded. *Get Your Kids Out Of Your Hair* was a brainchild of hers, a life-saver for parents who wanted to spend the early hours of Saturday in bed, without committing non-accidental injury to their children.

'Okay, *and* 3–2–1–, cue signature tune – '

'*We're going to get those kids right out of your hair . . .*'

Heidi stood on the edge of the set, watching. The two presenters were perched atop brightly coloured PVC dumb-bells. The signature tune faded away.

'Hi!' they both said in unison, flashing broad, toothy grins at their invisible audience. They looked very clean and very cute. Sally, who was dangerously close to her thirtieth birthday, was dressed in bright yellow and black polka dots, with pigtails and ankle socks and earrings like enormous sweets. Andy, her co-presenter, wore a jolly

Hawaiian shirt and red sneakers. He looked nauseatingly healthy.

'Hi kids!' said Sally, smiling broadly all the time. 'Coming up we've got another *Destruction of The Universe* cartoon. But first – Andy's going to be talking to Kelly Marie about her unusual pet – Andy.'

The cameras moved to focus on Andy's unwavering smile, while Sally slipped off the set and grabbed at the hip-flask that was held out for her. Someone else handed her a cigarette, ready lit. The make-up lady hovered over her with a powder puff but Sally pushed her impatiently aside. Away from the bright studio lights her make-up looked like orange putty, caking in the crow's feet around her eyes.

'Er, Sally . . .'

Sally's secretary appeared out of the gloom. She was a timid young girl, who looked barely older than the viewers of the programme.

'What is it?' demanded Sally, the giant liquorice all-sorts quivering against her cheeks.

'There's a phone call for you, I – '

'Christ, Emily! How many times do I have to tell you, I don't take calls while we're on air!' She blew out smoke in an angry puff. Emily coughed and retreated.

'*Silly little bitch!*' muttered Sally.

On the jolly plastic set, Andy, who received hundreds of fan letters each week in which fourteen-year-old girls offered to perform unmentionable sexual acts on him, was talking to Kelly-Marie about her pet tarantula. Kelly-Marie was a very well-developed thirteen-year-old.

The director sprang into action, making winding motions with his hands and holding up his fingers. 'Okay, kill the tarantula!'

Sally stubbed out her cigarette.

'And now – over to you, Sally!'

Sally positioned herself in front of the correct camera, remembering to grin. 'And now – it's time for *Destruction of the Universe*.'

The cartoon rolled up on the monitor screens. Sally's shoulders slumped and her smile faded. Andy asked Kelly-Marie for her phone number.

Heidi looked on from the shadows, fascinated. Emily, the secretary, materialised again. 'Heidi – message for you. Mike Marshall wants to see you in his office.'

Mike Marshall was the producer Heidi worked for, a tediously hearty man who spoke entirely in media clichés.

'Heidi – hi!' He saluted her with difficulty: he had a phone in each hand and two more propped behind each ear. He signalled to Heidi that she should wait.

'Sorry about that – LA on the line.' His ratty eyes gleamed behind their red-framed specs. Mike Marshall wasn't short-sighted, he wasn't long-sighted either; he just wore glasses because he thought they gave him more intellectual credibility than other TV types, while their bright colour proved that he did have a sense of humour.

'Heidi, look, I've got something very exciting lined up for you!' He beamed at her, waiting for her to show signs of excitement. She didn't.

'I'm going to take you off Programme Development for a while and use you to do some research for a documentary. We're putting together a show on Ivo Cathcart and you're going to be the key person in the team. I want you to spend some time with Cathcart and get some interviews down on tape.'

Heidi stared.

'You do know who he is, of course?'

She nodded.

'Well, come on then, what are you waiting for? This is a Golden Opportunity! He's the Darling of the Media, he's got the World at his Feet! It could be the Programme of the Century – '

'He looks like a pig,' said Heidi.

Mike Marshall tapped his pen impatiently. 'Heidi . . . look . . . I know things have been difficult for you lately. I know you've had pressures – ' he threw a meaningful look in the direction of the office across the hall. ' – all I'm saying is, you're due at the Rapier Industries Head Office at nine o'clock on Monday morning, for a preliminary interview with Ivo Cathcart. Be there!'

Heidi stumbled out into the corridor and was immediately locked into a half-nelson from behind.

'Charles . . . Jesus, you – '

He dragged her into his office and slammed the door shut behind them.

'*Mmmfgmnmnn* – ' Heidi tried to speak, but Charles' mouth plunged down on hers, snaking his tongue greedily between her teeth. They kissed voraciously, Heidi standing on tip-toe to do justice to his impressive six feet four.

'Aaah, my little Heidi! Oh God! That feels so good!' He slid his hand up the leg of her shorts. 'We've got to . . . meet soon.'

'Mmmm.' Heidi groaned her agreement. She pulled away. 'Look, I'm free tonight. How about it?'

Charles looked sorrowful. 'Love to sweetie, but I can't. Simply can't. It's my turn to babysit. One of Joy's dos. Mother's Union or something.'

There were footsteps in the corridor.

'Someone's coming, you'd better run. Love you.'

Before she could reply, Heidi found herself in the corridor again, with her lipstick smeared all over her chin.

Leofred Plunkett was standing in the queue in an Islington

Post Office. There was a red and yellow sign saying 'PLEASE QUEUE HERE' and the queue snaked back between dividing ropes as though they were waiting for admission to an important exhibition at the British Museum. For the amusement of the attendant thousands, there was a television set playing promotional videos.

'*Stuck for that perfect Xmas gift?*' enquired a blonde with perfect white teeth. '*Why not buy some of this stylish Post Office stationery? Available in white or azure. Ask at the counter . . .*'

'*Hi!*' said a handsome man in a suit, giving the camera a provocative smile. '*Got cash to spare? Why not invest in National Savings Certificates? Available at your Post Office, now!*'

And so it went on, proclaiming a variety of delights that could be procured if one ever reached the counter; happy, snowy-haired geriatrics with faultless dentures proclaiming the joys of Granny bonds, holidays on the Cornish Riviera, cassettes and records.

' "*These You Have Loved*" bring you "*Twenty Restaurant Classics*" – *great tunes you have hummed along to while eating Chicken Chow Mein. Featuring* "*Strangers in the Night*", "*Fernando*", "*Yesterday*" *and many, many more . . .*'

The customer at the counter finished licensing and taxing his car, filing a claim for a lost savings book, drawing his pension and sending several registered letters and moved on. The queue shuffled forward an inch. Leofred looked at his watch. There were countless people in front of him, and once he'd finished in the Post Office, he still had to go to a travel agent and buy a ticket before he met Heidi at one. He had hit upon the idea of withdrawing all his money from a long-forgotten Post Office savings account where he had deposited the amassed booty that had fallen out of Christmas and birthday cards for the last twenty years.

'*Stuck for that perfect Xmas gift?* . . .' The celluloid blonde was back again.

After the video had been round ten more times, Leofred reached the head of the queue at last. In front of him a man in a camouflage jacket and a woollen skull cap was handing over a long brown paper parcel that rather resembled a shotgun in shape.

'Where are you sending it to?' asked the girl behind the counter, without looking up. She was busy thumping bits of paper with her impressive array of franks.

'The Repobluc of Noithern Oireland' said the man, in a thick accent.

'Will that be first or second?'

Leofred stepped up to the counter and produced his battered savings book with a flourish. 'I'd like to withdraw all my savings please.'

'How much will the withdrawal be?' asked the girl, stamping a few more pieces of paper.

'All of it. All two hundred and seventy pounds.'

'You need to give a week's notice to draw out a sum of over fifty pounds.'

'But I don't have a week!' said Leofred desperately. 'In a week's time I hope to be up there, in the sky.' He pointed at the ceiling. The girl stared at him. 'I mean in an aeroplane.'

'In that case you'll have to fill in Form B38(a).'

Leofred looked around wildly for Form B38(a).

'They're the green ones, over there.' The girl pointed to a display counter at the back of the hall, near the door. Rows of forms, in all colours of the rainbow.

Leofred lowered his voice. 'Don't you keep any – er – under the counter?'

'You'll have to fill in Form B38(a) over there and bring it back.'

'You mean I have to queue again?'

'Yes. *Next!*'

Leofred had the promotional video word perfect by the time he left the Post Office clutching his money. He only had fifteen minutes left before his lunch appointment. He would be late now, whatever happened. Fortunately his trip to the travel agents was mercifully brief. Robyn had recommended he avoid large companies and use a bucket shop. 'It's the only way' she had told him as they travelled from Cambridge to London, 'To avoid the pitfalls of capitalism and beat the system.'

There was a likely looking place in Islington High Street, called Jingo Travel. On the walls faded posters of Ceylon vied for space with large-breasted pin-up girls. Pinioned behind impossibly tiny desks overflowing with schedules were three young Pakistanis, all talking on the phone at once.

'Oh no, sir!' They grinned as they apologised. 'You do not have enough for a flight to Los Angeles. Not for two hundred and seventy. This we cannot do, sir.' They shook their heads.

'Well, how much do I need?' asked Leofred, thinking of his embattled bank account.

'Oh . . . four hundred. At least four hundred.' The man grinned again.

'Four hundred, are you *sure?*'

'Unless . . .' he flicked through a battered white volume of figures and timetables that looked at least ten years out of date. ' . . . For three hundred and sixty you could go Nightmair . . . change at Cairo. That's the cheapest.'

'Thanks. Maybe I'll try somewhere else first, then – '

'Oh no, you won't get cheaper. Here, have my card.'

Leofred was thrust a business card that read '*JINGO TRAVEL – Mr Sammy*'. He put it in his pocket and set off at a jog towards the tube station, wondering how he was going to raise ninety pounds in a hurry.

*

In the Basmati Brasserie, Heidi was drumming her fingers on the table-cloth, and fuming. Leofred was late. Today, of all days, she was not in the mood to be kept waiting. Her morning at TV Mayhem had left her feeling less than charitable.

The Basmati Brasserie was an upmarket Indian Restaurant of chi-chi decor and indifferent food, frequented by those who wanted to be seen rather than devotees of oriental cuisine. Decorated completely in white, it had old colonial ceiling fans, splashing fountains amid lush greenery and a raucous parrot in a cage. The waiters padded silently about dressed in pantomime costumes, with turbans and slippers that curled up at the toes. This gave the pushy clientele the perfect excuse for treating them like slaves. Heidi dismantled a poppadom and stared at the entrance, waiting for Leofred to appear. Every now and then, one of the waiters would scowl at her as if to imply that she had been telling fibs when she said there would be two of them for lunch.

The double doors swung open and a couple came in, to a frenzy of bowing and scraping from the waiters. She was young and blonde and pretty and dressed in black from head to toe; he was thick-set, handsome in rather too obvious a way and dressed in expensive casual clothes. They were shown to a table behind Heidi and a bottle of champagne was brought straight away, seemingly without them having to order it.

One of the doors was opened a fraction and a pair of eyes looked suspiciously around the restaurant. They were followed by the rest of Leofred, trying to disguise the fact that he was out of breath. Heidi watched her younger brother descend the steps into the main area of the restaurant. Superficially the two of them looked very alike; the same tufty, colourless hair, the same grey eyes, the same smooth, sallow skin, but while Leofred's appearance was unfailingly neat and pressed, Heidi always managed to look dishevelled and disordered. Her clothes were either too small or too large, she frequently wore her knickers inside out and had she ever bothered to wear a petticoat, it would always have been showing. Hers was the air of the perpetual *gamine*, and although she was four years older than Leofred, they looked the same age.

'So,' said Heidi, after she had ordered a tandoori pheasant and jasmine-scented rice. 'Where are you staying? I was expecting you to ask if you could borrow my floor.'

Leofred pretended that his fingernails needed an urgent manicure. 'Well . . . ah . . . I met this girl – '

'A girl! Leofred, you old dog!' Heidi smirked into her spritzer.

'It was on the way down from Cambridge, actually. I didn't have enough money for the train, so I came on the coach and she . . . er . . . she came and sat next to me. She talked to me most of the way and then she said there was a room in her house in Canonbury if I wanted to borrow it, so I just, um, said yes.'

He shrugged helplessly. Heidi regarded him with incredulity. Her brother was always behaving in this way, just falling into situations. He wasn't a person who *did* things, he was a person things happened to.

'Well, well, well, so little old Leofred's not in the wicked metropolis five minutes and he gets himself shacked up with a woman! How on earth d'you do it?'

'It's not like that!' Leofred's face was bright red.

'Well, what is it like? What's *she* like?'

'Er, her name's Robyn. Quite nice, but rather bossy. She lives in a thing called a collective. She's a social worker.'

Heidi groaned.

There was a loud burst of laughter from the table behind them, and the sound of a second champagne cork popping.

Leofred glanced over his shoulder. 'Oh God!' he said, and buried his face in his *nargis kofta*.

'What is it?'

'That girl,' he hissed, 'I know her. She's at St Godbore's. Posie Fellowes. Dreadful hackette type.'

Posie gave another report of asinine laughter as she fed a piece of nan bread into the mouth of Jay Cathcart.

'Listen Heidi, I wanted to ask you a favour. Robyn wants me to ask you.'

'I'm not joining any women's bloody collective – '

'You don't have to join, just go to a meeting. Every week the members have to bring along a new person as a guest. I can't go because it's women only. I told Robyn I'd ask you.'

Heidi gave a snort of contempt. 'Forget it! I'm not going to some ghastly consciousness-raising session with women who drive 2CVs and don't shave their armpits.'

'Oh Heidi, please! She's been kind to me and I want to return the favour. It would only be for an hour or so. You never know, it might be interesting.'

'Oh, all right then,' Heidi said ungraciously. 'But only because I've got nothing better to do.'

She thought of Charles, who should have been cavorting beneath the sheets in her purple room in Kilburn Park, but instead would be minding his offspring. There was no reason why, *she*, Heidi, should sit at home and twiddle her thumbs just because his wimp of a wife had a yen to climb into her slingbacks and take off to a Tupperware party. Besides, her professional instincts urged, there might be a TV programme in it. And if so, perhaps Mike Marshall would let her off the Cathcart job.

At nine o'clock that evening, Heidi stood in a twilit street

29

in Islington, outside the headquarters of the North London Women's Sorority.

She couldn't quite believe that this was it. The seedy-looking Georgian terrace was almost derelict. Windows were boarded up, grass grew waist high in the gardens. A mangey cat roamed the dustbins; otherwise there was no sign of life. Heidi was beginning to feel distinctly uneasy. Leofred had assured her that Robyn would be there to meet her before the proceedings began, but in the meantime she could be robbed or mugged, or raped. One was forced to conclude that feminists didn't worry about such trifles, or else they carried machetes in their handbags.

Heidi reflected that 'handbag' was probably not correct terminology. Knapsacks?

'Greetings!' From out of nowhere an enormous figure appeared and clapped her on the back. 'You must be Heidi!'

Above the waist, Robyn Armitage was dressed for guerilla warfare, in a combat jacket and peaked camouflage hat. In contrast, from the waist down she was masquerading as a member of the under-fives, in baggy sugar-pink trousers and snub-nosed canvas playshoes. She was very fat, and the hair on her small head was cropped close, creating an oddly disproportionate effect. Like Heidi's boss at TV Mayhem, she wore glasses to improve her intellectual credibility; in this case gold-rimmed John Lennon specs.

'Ready for battle?' she cried gaily.

Heidi nodded.

'Let's go then!'

They plunged down into a dismal basement where, in a room lit only by a few candles in saucers, half a dozen women had already assembled. They all had short hair like Robyn's, and were dressed in what looked like outsize Babygros.

A tall woman with dark hair stood up and waved her

hands for silence. 'Right sisters, if you'd all like to be seated . . .'

Feeling desperately self-conscious, Heidi searched around for something to sit on.

'If you're looking for a chair,' whispered Robyn, 'We don't use them. Chairs were invented by men to keep women in a defined state of suspended animation. We use these – ' She pointed to a pile of polystyrene-filled sag-bags, ' – or we just squat, like the women of primitive tribes. It strengthens the pelvic floor, thus enabling us to have greater control of our bodily functions.'

Appalled, Heidi opted for sitting cross-legged on the very dirty floor. Robyn squatted down on her haunches, her vast pink behind looking not unlike one of the bean-bags.

The tall, dark woman was clearly the leader of the gang. She wore a baggy T-shirt sewn with sequins that read '*LITTLE MS MUFFET ATE THE SPIDER*'. Her hair was longer than that of her friends but she wore it scraped back from her head into a rubber band.

'That's Tharka,' whispered Robyn admiringly, 'She chose the name herself. Tharka was the Viking goddess of free spirits.'

'Okay, I'd like to open this meeting of the North London Women's Sorority,' said Tharka, 'For those of you who've never been before, it's just an informal exchange of ideas, problems and community information. First, can I say "Welcome sisters" to our guests. Perhaps you'd like to introduce yourselves and tell us a bit about you.'

'Hi, I'm Ruth,' said a girl in a bright orange boilersuit, 'And I'm currently involved in running One Womb, an alternative health centre in Hackney . . .'

With a sinking heart, Heidi waited for her own turn.

'I'm-Heidi-Plunkett' she mumbled quickly in the direction of her frivolous high-heeled shoes, 'And-I-work-in-TV.'

31

There were a few disapproving stares.

'We take it, of course,' Tharka gave her a patronising grin, 'that you concentrate your efforts on programmes concerning women's issues?'

'Er, sort of,' muttered Heidi.

'Great. Right, next on the agenda is our annual bazaar. We need some volunteers to get it organised – '

'Do we have to call it a "bazaar"?' queried Robyn. 'I mean, to me it just smacks of the historical repression of the Women's Institute, or the Mothers' Union.'

'Try thinking of the bazaar as an even older institution,' suggested someone else helpfully. 'An institution that's outside the network of repressive capitalism.'

'Right!'

The room was hot and airless. Heidi was beginning to feel sleepy. Her shoulders slumped and her eyelids drooped.

'Okay sisters, it's time for our job slot. I've been informed that there's a vacancy on the Women's Committee of the Borough Council. Twelve grand a year, plus expenses, plus a travel allowance. Anyone interested? Any of our guests like to sit on the Council? How about you, Heidi?'

'Er . . . what?' Heidi jerked awake.

'Do you have a knowledge of black and minority ethnic and political issues?'

'Um, not really.'

'Pity,' said Tharka, shaking her head and fixing Heidi with a beady stare. 'Are you an unmarried mother?'

'Ah . . . no.'

The position was eventually filled by Ruth, the witch doctor from Hackney. Tharka then squatted down in the circle with all the others. 'Okay, now it's time for us to discuss our personal problems. Does anyone feel they have something they have to get off their chest?'

Heidi's problem was trying to stay awake. Eventually a pale, pinched-looking girl spoke up.

'It's like . . . well, yeah, I do have a problem. I've fallen in love . . . with a man.'

There were unanimous intakes of breath.

'Okay, everyone, okay, calm down. It happens to a lot of us at some point in our lives. Now, look, Val,' Tharka lowered her voice to a gentle but persuasive pitch. 'To be male is to be deficient, emotionally limited. You know that as well as we do, you've just been temporarily blinded to the truth. Maleness is a disease. All males are emotional cripples. And oppressors, you have to remember that.'

'Think of wife-burning!' shouted one woman.

'Female circumcision!'

'And I expect he's married, isn't he?' asked Tharka.

The girl looked confused. 'I don't know. I suppose he could be.'

'Nine times out of ten they are. But don't worry, we can get you some therapy. Just don't worry.'

The girl smiled with gratitude through her tears. The other women embraced her silently, pitying her.

'Anyone else? How about you, Heidi?'

Christ, if they knew about Charles, they'd lynch me! And him! . . .

'I live alone,' said Heidi ambiguously.

'I've got some news,' said a plump girl, with a shy smile. 'Last week I had my final check-up at the Women's Artificial Insemination Centre and . . . I'm pregnant!'

There were general cries of pleasure and congratulation at this piece of news.

Tharka gave the expectant sister a munificent smile. 'We rejoice for you, that you have conceived without the degradation of heterosexual intercourse. And we look forward to hearing your thoughts and feelings on your pregnancy. We should all, as sisters, celebrate the sensuous and emotional pleasures of motherhood. It's our ability to reproduce ourselves that makes the male sex redundant.'

33

'And inadequate!'

'I reckon that's why they invented war. Because they couldn't breastfeed.'

There were murmurs of assent over this re-interpretation of the history of civilisation.

'I know!' said Robyn, her ample bottom rising like a cerise planet into a standing position. 'Let's celebrate by singing our anthem!'

There was cheering as the rest of the group rose and burst into song to the tune of 'Onward Christian soldiers'.

'Onward women militant, marching as to war! . . .'

A victory dance accompanied the song, involving a lot of swaying and thigh-slapping and pogo-ing on the spot.

'Fighting male oppression . . .'

Heidi stumbled around the room, buffeted by large, sweaty female bodies. She had removed her shoes earlier and they had now disappeared from sight. The dancing became wilder and less disciplined, the singing raucous.

'Let's cut off their foreskins . . .'

Heidi took advantage of the chaos. Carried by the boiler-suited tide to the foot of the stairs, she abandoned her shoes to the cause and fled.

In the kitchen of Robyn's house in Canonbury, Leofred was once more wondering how he could raise the extra ninety pounds. More, if he was to have a contingency fund of spending money. His bank wouldn't allow him an overdraft and would be unlikely to think that a trip to Hollywood created the need for a loan. And Heidi wouldn't have that sort of money spare, not unless she defrauded TV Mayhem. That only left his parents.

The trouble was, his parents were quite mad. His father barricaded himself in the bathroom and shot crows through the window with an air rifle. Behaviour which might have been acceptable if the house stood in its own country estate, but the view from the bathroom window was of a suburban street in Sidcup. His mother was too preoccupied with her own hobby horses to care, the most demanding of which was making papier mâché replicas of ancient burial mounds.

It was time to go to bed. Leofred made himself a cup of cocoa and carried it up to the room that had been lent to him. There was a hard, narrow bed in the corner, and the walls were decorated with posters of enormous women clutching men's decapitated heads. Something on the floor looked suspiciously like mouse droppings.

He had almost finished undressing when the door burst open and Robyn staggered in. Leofred stood in the middle of the room, holding his shirt by one sleeve so that it would shield his bunchy grey Y-fronts.

'Er . . .'

'Hi!' Robyn didn't seem to notice that he was about to get into bed. Her eyes were glazed and she seemed excited, euphoric.

'Did it go well, your meeting?'

'Yeah, great!'

'How about Heidi? Did she enjoy it?'

'Yeah, she seemed to get really into it.' Robyn sounded vague. 'Listen, come down to the kitchen for a drink. The night is still young.'

'Well, I was just getting into bed actually . . . I'll have to put my clothes on again . . .'

Leofred hoped that if he delayed long enough she would give up.

'Oh, don't bother with that. Come as you are!'

'Perhaps you could lend me a dressing gown?' Robyn was sure to wear a man's robe, he thought.

'Sure.'

She disappeared and came back with a quilted nylon housecoat, high-waisted and lace trimmed. Leofred put it on with some repugnance, which Robyn didn't seem to notice, and followed her downstairs to the kitchen. One drink; he'd just have one drink to humour her, then he'd take off this ridiculous object and go to bed.

The house was unnaturally quiet. Perhaps one of the other women would come back and create a diversion. He presumed there *were* others, since Robyn had originally described her home to him as a 'free, non-hierarchical collective'.

'I expect the others will be coming in soon from their various . . . activities?' he remarked casually as Robyn found a bottle and glasses and poured out two measures of an evil, green liquid.

'No, actually. They're all away at the Barnham peace camp, protesting about the development of a new Rapier Hyperstore in a conservation area.' She laughed. 'God, you don't think I'd let you stay here if I wasn't alone? No male overnight guests. It's the only house rule. That and a compulsory monthly contribution to the Feminine Hygiene fund.'

'Oh, I see.' Leofred gulped the disgusting, sticky liquid.

'Oregano wine.' said Robyn with satisfaction. 'Herbal. Organic. Hypo-allergenic. Drink up!' She poured him another glass, and one for herself. 'So . . .' she pulled her chair up close to the table so that their knees brushed. 'So . . . have you solved your money problem yet?'

Leofred shook his head.

'Well, of course, we all know what a woman would do if she was in that situation ∴ . .' Leofred didn't know, but before he could find out, Robyn went on: 'I suppose you're dying to know why I joined the Women's Movement?' She gave him a suggestive smile and poured herself another glass of oregano wine. 'I'll tell you about it, shall I? It was

36

about ten years ago. I lived in Hampshire with Mummy and Daddy, in a nice house with a big garden and a daily woman. I had a pony. I even belonged to the bloody Pony Club. Can you believe it?'

Leofred couldn't picture Robyn astride a pony without feeling extreme compassion for the beast.

She took another gulp of wine. 'When I was about sixteen or seventeen I started being asked out to dances. One summer I was asked to the Yacht Club dance. I was really excited. Spent *hours* getting myself ready. I put my hair in Carmen rollers, got it all nicely flicked back. Put on my best sky-blue polyester halter-neck dress with matching sling-back platform shoes. And make-up. Just a touch of pearly-blue eyeshadow. Candy-pink lipstick. I felt like a fucking princess.'

Robyn took yet another slurp of wine. By now she had dispensed with her glass and was drinking straight from the bottle. Her bright pink thigh pressed heavily against Leofred's quilted one. 'We bopped the night away to Sweet and the Bay City Rollers. There was one guy in particular who took my fancy. He was sort of small and dark, bit like Dustin Hoffman. He seemed to like me. We danced quite a bit, and then he offered me a lift home. He'd borrowed his mum's Mini Traveller. He got out to open the door for me and I thought "What a gentleman!" I asked him if he'd like to come in for a coffee and he said no, sorry, he had to get home.

'So I said, "Aren't you even going to give me a goodnight snog?" And do you know what he did? Can you imagine?'

Leofred couldn't.

'He laughed. He laughed, right in my face. "Thank you, sweetheart," he said ". . . but you're not exactly my type." "Why not?" I asked. He laughed again and he said – he said "Have you looked at yourself in the mirror recently?" 'And d'you know what I did? I went out into the garden

37

that same night and built a bonfire. I threw my blue poly-ester halter-neck and my platforms onto the blaze. And the Carmen rollers. And then I went and looked through all the W's in the Yellow Pages until I found what I was looking for. And ever since then I've been quite happy.'

'So you don't really need men at all?' asked Leofred hopefully, wondering how he could move his chair to the right without making it look as if that was what he was trying to do.

Robyn took another mouthful of oregano wine and sucked it through her teeth. 'Oh, I wouldn't say that,' she mumbled, leaning closer, 'There are still some things a woman needs that battery-operated devices alone can't provide. And you know something, you're really rather sweet. You're not into this aggressive, macho thing. And you're quite good-looking . . .'

She was practically on top of him now, and her hand was edging its way inside the lace-trimmed robe. ' . . . 'Course, we're not supposed to. But while the others are away . . .'

Leofred tried to speak but his mouth was put out of action by Robyn's. The wire rims of her glasses pressed into his cheeks. Underneath the dressing gown, her hand was snaking about and she gave little 'oohs' and 'ahs' of delight like a child discovering the contents of its Christmas stocking.

'Come on, off with these!'

Leofred felt a quick tug, then Robyn was waving his grey jockeys above her head like a trophy.

The next thing he knew, he was flat on his back on the bed upstairs, being suffocated by a large pair of breasts, and Robyn was wriggling around on top of him making a lot of squelching noises that he would have much preferred not to hear.

He was still wearing the quilted housecoat, and the decapitated men on the walls looked down on him in horror.

*

A few miles away, in a fashionable square near Primrose Hill, Tharka, Viking goddess of free spirits, was parking her car – a large Volvo. Still in the driving seat, she stripped off her *Ms Muffet* T-shirt and replaced it with a Laura Ashley blouse that had been stuffed into the glove compartment. Then, as Mrs Joy Jolyon, she unlocked the front door of her house.

Glancing through the door of the drawing room, she saw her husband Charles asleep in front of the television, a half-empty bottle of scotch at his feet. His head was thrown back and he was snoring loudly.

Joy gave a contemptuous laugh and went upstairs to check on the children.

Three

There's fifty thousand pounds for you in a numbered Swiss bank account if you'll go down on me . . .

As Ivo Cathcart and Heidi Plunkett faced one another across his massive desk, Heidi was thinking about how ugly he was. Ivo was thinking about sex.

It was nine o'clock on Monday morning and they were at the head office of Rapier Industries.

'Sit down.' Ivo pointed to a large black chair.

'It's all right, I'll stand.'

Fine, thought Ivo. *That way I can get a better view of your body . . .*

He hadn't been able to believe his luck when he saw Heidi. She was exactly the type that got him going. Not pretty, but appealing, with her terrier-like little features and dusty-coloured hair that stood up on end. And she was young, probably a little immature too, judging by the aggressive attitude she adopted. There was a provokingly healthy look to her; strong, sinewy, energetic . . . horny. She had great little tits too, upturned like snouts, like puppy dogs' noses.

He wondered how much it would cost him to get a better look at them. Ivo was used to getting exactly what he wanted, simply by buying it. He was sure this girl was no exception.

'I'm here on behalf of Mike Marshall at TV Mayhem,' she was saying, 'We want to set up a series of interviews with you as the basis for a documentary we're going to put together.'

Heidi didn't mention that she was supposed to be doing the interviews. She was still hoping to get out of it.

'I see . . .' Cathcart stood up and moved around the room, picking up a huge lighter and then a cigarette from a silver box. He lit the cigarette. Beneath his grotesque, pig-like head, Cathcart's skin was pink and raw as though it had been sunburned. ('Like bacon,' thought Heidi.) He had a trim and muscular body, impressive even, and moved in a terse and economical way as though he were holding in his energy the way someone holds their breath.

'Are *you* going to be interviewing me?' he demanded.

Not if I can help it . . .

'It's unlikely. I'm very, er . . . junior.'

'Never mind, we can soon change that. Tell your Mr Marshall I shall withdraw my co-operation unless you, personally, conduct the interviews. In fact we'll tell him now, shall we?'

With a deft flick of the wrist, seemingly without even looking, Ivo pressed a button on an impressive console. There was a buzz and a light flashed. He gave the order.

Heidi seethed inwardly.

'We'll start this afternoon.'

'I can't. I'm going to a wedding.'

'Cancel.'

Heidi glared at him. 'I've no intention of cancelling.'

Ivo watched the Minnie Mouse bow in her hair vibrate, positively *bristle* with resentment.

Great, I like them stroppy. And I bet she lives in some seedy bedsit somewhere with her little white girlie knickers drying on the radiator . . .

She refused to meet his gaze, staring instead at the photograph of a beautiful blonde that stood on his desk.

'My wife. She's a complete bitch,' he said cheerfully. 'So, where's this wedding? I'll have a company limo drive you there.'

'What, all the way to East Grinstead?' sneered Heidi. 'I'll get there under my own steam, thank you very much.'

'Okay, okay.' Ivo was unruffled.

Sixty grand. No, make it seventy-five. Seventy-five thousand pounds just to lift your T-shirt and let me see those cute little boobs . . .

The door opened and a young man breezed in, apparently unannounced. He was wearing a baby-pink Lacoste shirt, designer jeans and a gold watch the size of a small plate. Heidi recognised him as the champagne swiller from the Basmati Brasserie.

'I'd like you to meet my younger brother, Jay Cathcart. He's in charge of our Far Eastern operation. Jay, this is Miss Heidi Plunkett.'

At least he'd remembered her name.

Jay held out his hand 'Heyy!' he said with a mock-Dixieland accent.

Christ, what a jerk! Heidi was beginning to feel uncomfortable. She was hot; there was sweat breaking out on her upper lip. Her legs had disappeared up to the ankles, so deep was the executive shag pile. It tickled her bare flesh. She felt suffocated by the wealth of it all, by its bigness. Big deals, big bank accounts, big egos.

'Look, I won't hold you up any longer Mr Cathcart,' she said hurriedly, desperate for escape. 'I'll telephone your secretary and set up some dates.'

She tried to walk quickly to the door, but the carpet was so deep, it was impossible. Next time, she thought, I'll bring my snow shoes.

*

Leofred Plunkett was just waking up after a bad dream. He had been dreaming that he was drowning in an icy sea, and just as he managed to reach the surface, a whale swam along and smothered him.

Wait a minute! He was awake, wasn't he? But the whale was still there. It was lying on his face. It gave a snort and moved away. Robyn's cropped head popped up from beneath the covers.

She was lying right in the middle of an extremely narrow single bed, with Leofred perched vertically along its edge, like a piece of fencing. He didn't know whether to laugh or cry.

They lay there for a few moments, contemplating the awfulness of what had happened. Leofred wasn't aware of having *done* anything. He tried not to think about it. He tried instead to think about how he was going to raise one hundred pounds, or thereabouts.

'Er, Robyn . . .' he said, 'do you remember what you said last night about – '

'Said last night about what?' snapped Robyn. She had a hangover. 'If you mean what I said about needing a man, it was all lies, rubbish. I was temporarily deranged. Strong women don't need men. Never have done and never will do.'

'No,' explained Leofred, 'I mean about what women do when they're short of money. You said it was obvious. And I wanted to know. What they'd do, I mean.'

Robyn straightened herself up against the pillows and gave him a withering stare. 'They'd go on the game, of course!'

Heidi was sitting in a train at Victoria Station, waiting for it to take her to East Grinstead. The trouble was, it didn't move. The guard blew his whistle, the train gave a bilious jerk, then stood still. A few minutes later, it moved again, getting half-way down the platform. All the passengers heaved a sigh of relief. Then it stopped again and didn't move for another fifteen minutes, by which time its passengers could have caught the later train to East Grinstead and still have arrived there sooner.

Heidi looked at her watch, cursing under her breath. The wedding started in an hour, and when she got to East Grinstead station, she still had to find a taxi to take her to the church, some three or four miles away. It was hot and stuffy in the carriage, and she could feel the trail of sweat down her back and under her arms, leaving damp patches on her wedding finery.

Heidi didn't have many dresses – she wasn't the sort of girl who wore them – and the only one that was clean was a simple white cotton shift with kick pleats in its long skirt. She didn't possess a hat, but she'd wired a white flower into her short, tufty hair and found a pair of white tights.

There was now a ladder racing up their left leg. Swearing, she pulled them off and put them in her handbag. The pile of the British Rail seat covers scratched her bare legs like five days' worth of stubble. She put the tights on again, back to front so that the ladder wouldn't be so obvious. Then she fished a can of lager out of her bag, put her feet up on the seat in front of her and closed her eyes for the satisfying 'crack' of the tag as she pulled it open.

She reflected that it had been on just such a journey that Josie had met her bridegroom, Michael. She had been travelling between Paddington and Oxford one Sunday and every compartment had been full of serious Americans on their way to admire the splendours of that city. Michael had been the one sitting opposite her, who had leaned forward and asked her one of the clues in the *Herald Tribune* crossword. Of course Josie hadn't been able to help him.

44

She scarcely had the intellect for the Quick Teaser in the *News of the World*. She confided in Heidi afterwards that what had impressed her most about him was the fact that he was filling in the crossword not with a pencil, or with a biro, but with a Montblanc fountain pen.

Heidi had been surprised at their engagement. She had never thought of Josie as the marrying kind. It wasn't that she didn't like men, but that she seemed to like *all* men. She had been sent off to Florence to be 'finished off' at the British Institute. The only Italian she knew when she left England were the words from the libretto of Tosca: '*Cosi, cosi ti voglio*' – 'Like this, I want you like this'. When she returned to England three heady months later, they were still the only Italian words she knew, but they seemed to have proved very useful.

Heidi didn't have to wait long for a taxi, but even so, she was very late arriving at the church. Six small bridesmaids, dressed in pink taffeta replicas of Lady Diana Spencer's wedding dress, were jumping up and down on the steps in excitement, while various male relatives in morning suits looked out anxiously at the road. The black cab rumbled to a stop at the church gate and Heidi scrambled out, clutching the flower that had fallen out of her hair.

'Oh look, there's the bride!' said one of the crowd of onlookers who had gathered in the street to watch.

'I am *not* the bride!' said Heidi crossly, stamping up the path and into the church. She was just in time to squeeze into a back pew with the old ladies of the parish, who are never invited but come along just to ogle, when Josie sailed down the aisle in enough white net to fill a whole suburban street with curtains.

The reception was held at Josie's family home, in a pink-lined marquee built around the swimming pool. Her parents had a 1930s ranch house on the edge of the Ashdown Forest, complete with Filipino maid, tennis court and a swinging garden seat where Josie made her early forays into the mysterious union of the sexes with boys from the local tennis club.

Today all that was forgotten, although the noisy and over-confident young men in rented morning suits with silver cravats, like stand-ins from a wedding scene in *Dallas*, probably had several of Josie's former beaux among their number.

Heidi was met at the entrance to the marquee by a black-clad caterer who thrust a lukewarm glass of anonymous 'fizz' into her hand and instructed her to leave her gift in the alcove on the right. A table groaned under the weight of large, tastefully wrapped parcels with ribbon rosettes on top. They looked like the sort of presents that languish under the Christmas tree in the windows of banks and building societies; presents that everyone except the very young knows are just empty cardboard boxes.

Heidi fished in her handbag for her present but couldn't find it amongst all the junk. She pulled out the empty lager can and screwed-up paper tissue and, finally, the gift. It was a small phial of scent called *MANTRAP* – ' . . . *will drive your man wild in bed.*' She laid it reverently amongst the soup tureens and vegetable dishes from Harrods, with the empty lager can beside it, and went to join the crowds, braying louder than ever now they were on the third round of 'fizz'.

Standing in one corner near the mountainous buffet, she waited for the onslaught of the 'randy uncle syndrome', so familiar at weddings and other family parties. It didn't take long.

'Hullo there!' said a red-faced man with thinning hair, who was bursting out of a musty morning suit. He was already sozzled. 'Well then, what's a pretty young lady like you doing here all alone, why don't we just go and find a table somewhere, somewhere quiet, just – '

His voice dribbled off into an incoherent moan. He tried to place his left hand on Heidi's buttock, but missed and grabbed the corner of the buffet table instead. A large pineapple rolled off the fruit display and landed on his foot. Heidi had already moved on.

She drifted aimlessly, trying to avoid the crowd of noisy young men who were busy dipping the ends of one another's cravats in their glasses of champagne. She really only wanted to talk to Josie, who had once been her bosom buddy, sharing Rod Stewart records and illicit Embassy filter-tipped, comparing love-bites.

Eventually she spotted Josie on the other side of the marquee. She was clinging tightly to the sleeve of a morning suit that did not belong to her new husband, and giving its wearer a wet kiss on the mouth. Josie saw her and waved a net-gloved hand.

'So,' she said, a flush of triumph on her plump face, 'when's it going to be your turn?'

Heidi shrugged. 'Dunno.'

'Who are you going out with these days?' persisted Josie. 'You're not still with that – ' She lowered her voice; since it was a dirty word at this celebration of wedded bliss, ' – *married man?*'

Heidi nodded.

'Oh Heid, honestly, isn't it time you found someone *suitable?* There are loads of yummy single men here today. Let me just – '

'Yes, I saw you sampling one of them a moment ago. Anyway, he is suitable,' said Heidi. 'He's far more suitable than most of those idiots over there.' She indicated the ex-tennis club beaux playing frisbee with the bread rolls. 'He doesn't get drunk and make a fool of himself. He's more . . . mature. That's what I want.'

'Oh well, have it your way.' Josie shrugged. The seams of her net extravaganza creaked, 'Christ Heidi, I don't know how much longer this thing's going to go on, but I can't wait to get out of this dress!'

Heidi noted her friend's plump midriff. 'Mmm, it is rather tight. Didn't you have a fitting?'

'Yes – three months ago.' Josie giggled. 'Promise you won't tell anyone, but I'm p-r-e-g-n-a-n-t. Four months!'

'Josie! Doesn't anyone know?'

'I didn't *dare* tell Mum, not before the wedding. She'd have had a fit! She certainly wouldn't have let me float up the aisle in a long white dress. But once the wedding's out of the way – *well*, she'll come round in the end . . . Oh God Heidi, I think I'm going to throw up.'

Heidi helped Josie to her parents' bathroom and waited in the bedroom while she made very un-bridal noises over the lavatory pan. Beside Mrs Pearce's bed was a large studio portrait of a dimpled Josie, age three, looking as though butter wouldn't melt in her mouth. Heidi laughed. Next to the photograph was a telephone . . . She stared at it. She wanted to talk to Charles. Weddings always made her clingy. He had said he would be working alone at home today, perhaps . . .

She cocked one ear to the bathroom. From the sound of it, Josie still had a few canapés to go. She picked up the receiver and dialled.

'Charles – hi, it's me!' she whispered.

'Oh, er, hullo.' His voice sounded strange.

'Charles, I miss you. Can we get together sometime? Soon.'

'Yes, okay, let's do that.' He sounded more as if he was in the boardroom than in his study at home.

'How about tonight?' Heidi pressed her mouth close to the receiver.

'Tonight? Could do, yes. About eight thirty?'

There was a sound of flushing and taps running in the bathroom.

'*Come over to my place*,' hissed Heidi and slammed the phone down just as Josie came back into the bedroom, as green as the trailing ivy in her bouquet.

At five-thirty the bride and groom left for their honeymoon, Josie looking portly in a tailored suit. Heidi lined up obediently on the steps with the other unmarried or unmarriageable girls, failed to catch the bouquet and then went off in search of someone to give her a lift to East Grinstead station. Perhaps one of the tennis club hearties. They all seemed to own Golf GTIs, parked with casual randomness in the forecourt.

'Miss Plunkett,' said one of the black-shrouded caterers, coming after her, 'Miss Plunkett, I have just received a message to say that your car is ready for you.'

'My *car*? But I don't have a car.'

'You are Miss Heidi Plunkett?' asked the woman.

'Yes, but – '

'In that case your car is waiting for you at the bottom of the drive.'

Heidi hobbled down the drive in court shoes that were beginning to slice into her hot, puffy feet.

Then she saw it, and just stood and stared. It was a long white Bentley, gleaming in the early evening sunshine like a slug flushed out by rain. The windows were tinted, so Heidi couldn't see who, if anyone, was inside. She hobbled nearer. The rear window slid down, operated by an electric switch.

'Oh God, not you!' she said.

It was him. Pig Face.

'I thought you might like a lift back.' He looked down at her swollen feet, as porcine as his face. 'In an air-conditioned car.'

Heidi was now in the throes of an early evening hangover from excesses of poor quality Iberian 'fizz', and therefore not in the mood to argue. She flung herself onto the back

49

seat next to Ivo Cathcart and tugged off her shoes. He nodded to the chauffeur and the car slid on its slug-like way.

'I won't ask you how you found me.'

'No need to really, is there?' Ivo said with irrepressible cheerfulness, 'Monday isn't exactly a popular day for weddings. And you did say East Grinstead. There was only one.'

He pressed a button on the door and a wooden panel slid open to reveal a bar. 'Champagne?' he offered, as if he knew it would make her sick.

'God, no!' she said rudely. 'Have you got a cold beer?'

'We don't seem to carry beer, I'm afraid.'

'In that case I'll have nothing.'

But Ivo ordered the car to stop at the next off-licence they passed and the chauffeur went in and purchased a can of ice-cold malt, carrying it disdainfully in his gloved hand.

Heidi drank it in silence while Ivo fiddled with a computer VDU that appeared at the touch of a button.

'Just checking the Rapier share price,' he said. 'And I'll bet you anything you like it's gone up since last week.'

It had.

'How did you know?' Heidi demanded, intrigued.

'My wife had another son last week. It makes me look secure. And my own image is so tied up with the image of the company, that whatever happens in my private life affects the share price. It's as simple as that.'

'I thought you said you hated your wife.'

'I didn't say that. I said she was a bitch. Which she is. Probably isn't even my baby anyway. But the public doesn't know that.'

Heidi stared at him, appalled. He really was monstrous. He hadn't betrayed the slightest flicker of regret, or concern even. 'Why doesn't she leave?'

'Why should she? She's got a million a year, tax free. She's laughing.'

Ivo picked up his cell-phone, tossed it up in the air and caught it the right way round with the same hand. He dialled Tokyo to find out where the yen closed. At the same time the other hand was alternating sips of scotch and drags on a cigarette.

'Why don't you leave *her?*'

'Why? There's no incentive to do so, that's why. But I don't want any of this going into my TV profile. That's one of the things I wanted to see you about. As far as the public's concerned, Linda and I are the perfect couple, d'you understand? . . . Also, I have a business proposition I want to put to you.'

Ivo rested his left hand on Heidi's forearm, while his right continued punching figures into the computer keyboard. It was as if the two parts of his brain weren't connected. 'I'm sure that a young working girl like you is struggling to make ends meet. You probably can't even afford a mortgage, right?'

Heidi gave him a furious stare.

'Look, I'm prepared to give you the money for a flat of your own, perhaps a nice car, an option on some Rapier shares . . .'

'Come on, get to the point.'

'All you have to do is let me put my hand up that little white skirt of yours and into your knickers. That's all. You don't even have to screw me. Just let me . . . just one hand – '

'And what's the other hand going to be doing? Checking the New York commodities market?' Heidi brushed his hand off her arm. 'Let me say this, Mr Cathcart, for the first and last time. I have a man in my life already. He's sweet and kind and gentle and . . .'

She wondered how far she could spin out Charles' virtues.

' . . . and sincere. But even if I didn't, I wouldn't let you near my underwear! Because I don't fancy you, I don't even like you. In fact . . .'

Ivo was still smiling slightly, apparently quite unfazed.

' . . . Oh, what's the point! Stop the car! I SAID "STOP THE CAR"!' she bawled at the driver.

The Bentley screeched to a halt and she scrambled out into a ditch, somewhere near South Croydon. Ivo's window slid down.

' . . . And don't bother trying to talk me into getting in the car again – '

'I wasn't going to,' said Ivo smoothly. He passed her white court shoes out through the open window. 'But if you're going to walk to London, you'll need these.'

When Heidi telephoned, Charles Jolyon was in the bedroom, rubbing body oil into his wife's legs.

It wasn't the way he would have chosen to spend the afternoon, and he did have a lot of work to do, but in her usual bullish way, she had insisted.

Joy/Tharka was lying face down on the marital bed, stark naked. Her tall, strong body glistened. Downstairs in the stripped pine kitchen, the Swedish *au pair* was reading non-racist fairy stories to the two children, Thaddeus and Clytemnestra.

'Rub some more into the backs of my thighs . . . okay, okay, it's just to moisturise my skin, not to bring me to the heights of sexual arousal.'

'Sorry darling.'

'Right, now do the other side.'

On his hands and knees, Charles shuffled over the carpet

to the other side of the bed. It was at that moment that the phone began to ring, though it would have been more prudent to let the *au pair* answer it than to smear the handset with massage oil.

'Who was that?' demanded Joy.

'Oh . . . work. Ah . . . unscheduled meeting this evening. The Cathcart project.'

'Well, you'll have to call them back and tell them you can't go, won't you? I'm going out and it's Helga's night for her self-defence classes.'

'But darling – '

'I said call them back! Go on – you might as well do it now.'

Sighing, Charles picked up the oily handset and asked the TV Mayhem switchboard to put him through to his mystified secretary.

'Megan, just calling you back after you . . . called me.'

'I what? Sorry, is – '

Charles blundered on. 'That meeting tonight at eight thirty. Cancel it, will you?'

'What mee – '

Charles hung up. 'There. Satisfied?'

'More oil on my back, please.'

Plucking up courage, he asked, 'Won't you at least tell me why you have to go out?'

'No.'

'I'm beginning to suspect you've got another man.'

Joy twisted onto her back and gave him a pitying sneer.

'Don't be ridiculous!' she said.

Leofred Plunkett was standing on a street in the heart of the West End, offering his body for sale.

He had concluded that it was the only way of raising

cash in a hurry, and if Robyn's friends could do it, why couldn't he?

'But isn't the exploitation of women's bodies exactly what you oppose?' he had asked gingerly.

'Listen kiddo,' Robyn had adopted a very superior tone, 'who's being exploited – the woman, who's in control, or the dumb trick who's coughing up the money?'

'Well, if women can do it, I don't see why men shouldn't. Where do you think I should, er . . . stand?'

'You're not going dressed like that, are you?' Robyn had pointed derisively at his *Man at C&A* cords and inoffensive plaid shirt.

'Why not? I've ironed them.'

'Come *on*, if you want to play the game, you've got to play by the rules! You've got to try and look a little sexy! D'you think women go and stand on street corners wearing tweed suits? You want to show off your wares. Get yourself some cute little shorts, something like that.'

Leofred went into Lillywhites and bought a pair of red satin athletics shorts with slits up the sides and a vest with Mickey Mouse on it. Fearing that his knobbly knees might deter prospective punters, he also purchased a pair of skateboarding knee-pads. Then he stood outside the entrance to the Cafe Royal in Piccadilly, adopting what he hoped was a business-like attitude.

It began to grow dark. Nothing happened. Leofred smiled at female passers-by, but they all looked away and hurried on. One or two men slowed down and gave him a suggestive smile, but Leofred was adamant that he was not going to take male customers. He wasn't so desperate that he had to sink to that.

An attractive young woman slowed down, smiling at him.

'Hey, baby!' he said in a rather feeble imitation of a West Coast drawl. Robyn had told him that he should give 'a verbal come-on'.

'Excuse me – do you have the time?'

'It's quarter to ten.'

'Thank you very much.' She moved on.

Some minutes later, a foreign-looking woman stopped. 'Excuse me – you know the time, pliss?'

'Ten o'clock.' Leofred was just beginning to wonder whether he wouldn't have had more success auditioning for the Speaking Clock, when an elderly lady tugged at his arm. She was smartly dressed and well-coiffed, carrying a large lizard-skin handbag.

'Young man,' she said. 'Do you? . . . Are you? . . .'

'Yes,' said Leofred, wondering if it was too late to impose an upper age limit, but so anxious to get off the street that he felt he'd try anything.

'I need your services in something very special,' she said, 'How much?'

'Ah . . . two hundred pounds. Cash.'

'Very well. My place. It's just around the corner.'

After looking about her furtively, the old lady tucked her arm into the crook of Leofred's and led him down the street to a smart block of mansion flats.

'Nice weather, isn't it?' she asked politely as they stood in the lift waiting for it to arrive at the fifth floor.

Leofred looked at her. She was at least seventy. Her gnarled hands, adorned with old-fashioned rings, had liver spots on them.

He stared down at his knee-pads. 'Um, madam . . . I've been thinking . . . perhaps you'd prefer someone a little older.'

'Oh gracious, it's not for me, dear. It's for my little girl.'

Oh God, thought Leofred, this is even worse . . .

'You're about to meet my little girl,' she said as she clanged the lift door shut and unlocked the door of her flat, ' . . . I want the two of you to have a very special relationship.'

Her 'little girl' turned out to be a motheaten old poodle with wind. It was sitting at the centre of the chintzy, over-furnished room on a large pink cushion. There was a pink ribbon tied around its neck.

'This is my baby,' said the woman, with abundant pride. 'Isn't she lovely? Now – ' She removed her coat and hat and settled herself in an armchair opposite the dog. 'I want you to make love to my darling.'

'*Make love to her!*'

The woman tut-tutted. 'Oh . . . you young people are all alike! Born into the permissive age of the sixties and obsessed with lechery ever after. I meant, pay court to her.'

'Ah.' Leofred stared at the dog, then patted it tentatively on its grizzled head.

'She's very sensitive. I want you to talk nicely to her.'

'Hullo, little doggie.'

'Not like that! I want you to describe what you'd like to do to her.'

'Well . . . I'd sort of stroke her furry ears, and – '

'No, no, you must whisper it!'

'*I'd sort of stroke her furry little ears and – *'

'No, no no, you're supposed to be talking to *her*!'

Leofred turned back to the poodle. Fixing its gaze with his own, he drew in his breath and began. 'I'd like to stroke your furry little ears . . . and tickle you under the chin – '

'That's right!' exclaimed the old lady with satisfaction, pouring herself a sweet sherry and putting her feet up on a pink Dralon footstool. The dog farted mournfully.

'I'd like to take you for lovely long walks through piles of dry leaves . . . I'd like to give you a lamp-post all of your very own . . .'

An hour later, Leofred escaped with twenty ten-pound notes stuffed down the front of his red satin shorts. The old lady had been completely satisfied with his perform-ance, but the poodle remained unmoved throughout.

He went back to Robyn's house and stripped off the clothes of his profession, bundling them into a carrier bag in the corner of the room. The bank notes he put in an envelope with the cash he had drawn out of his Post Office savings account. Then he took out his cheque book and with great satisfaction wrote a cheque for three hundred and sixty pounds to Jingo Travel.

That night he fell asleep with a smile on his face. He *wasn't* dull-witted and unadventurous, that was now official. He had just made two hundred pounds by talking to a dog. And he was on his way to Hollywood.

In Grafton Road, a miserable Heidi was sitting on the edge of her bed, waiting for Charles. He was often late, but he'd never been *this* late before.

She poured herself a drink, paced the room. Switched on the TV, switched it off. Switched it on again.

'... and tonight, Rapier Industries chief, Ivo Cathcart, has announced the acquisition of a massive factory complex outside Kawasaki in Japan. Cathcart, thirty-two, hopes to break into the video games market ...'

A still photograph of Ivo Cathcart's grinning pink face flashed up on the screen. Heidi threw a shoe at it. She went on lobbing missiles until she hit the 'off' button. Then she began her pacing again.

The phone rang. Heidi leapt on it.

'Darling, it's me.' Charles was whispering.

'Why are you whispering?' demanded Heidi. 'Why aren't you here?'

'My wife's ... ill, and both the kids have come down with a virus. I have to be here.'

'Where's the bloody au pair?'

'She's out. Listen, I am sorry darling, I – '

Heidi tried to slam the phone down, but couldn't. The wire had got tangled around the white cotton dress she had been wearing that afternoon. She ripped the dress away from her, scattering buttons, and with a howl of rage hurled it out of the open window.

It drifted over the garden gate and floated down Grafton Road like a small, shapeless ghost.

At the headquarters of Rapier, there was still one light on.

Ivo Cathcart was in his office. He was sitting at his desk, staring at the photograph of his wife and thinking about Heidi Plunkett in her white cotton dress. He lusted after her. He ached for her. Failing to buy her had inflamed his passion to an unbearable pitch.

From the chunky glass and chrome frame, Linda smiled broadly as though someone were massaging the small of her back. In so many ways she was the perfect wife. Not frumpy or homely, but tall and elegant and clever; an ex-graphic designer. She wore her blonde hair long and loose, a few contemporary pieces of jewellery, casual designer clothes. She was mature and confident, capable of managing a large house, entertaining, raising three children.

But much as he needed that sort of wife, Ivo couldn't get excited by her. The cool, sleek Linda, her figure still trim, slipping from the bathroom in her lace-trimmed Janet Reger nightdress and matching negligee, smelling subtly of *Opium* or *Youth Dew*, just made him feel depressed and caged. Never aroused. At first it had been a silent taboo between them and they had pretended with a lot of demonstrative kisses and 'my darling's, but gradually cold war set in. She didn't care about no longer exciting him, and she let him know it.

And Ivo started to fall prey to violent fantasies about

young, chunky female bodies clad in cheap chain-store clothes. Girls with un-waxed legs and bikini lines, who didn't have a facial every week, girls with grubby or chewed fingernails.

He sat at his desk and he dreamed of Heidi, sleeping in some lumpy single bed surrounded by teddy bears and girlish untidiness. He wanted to run amok in her young life, bellowing like a bull, taking, grabbing, possessing . . .

Christ, this would have to stop! He needed to talk to someone. The only person he knew certain to be up at this hour was Jay. He pressed a button and the phone found the number in its memory.

As the receiver was picked up at the other end, there were immediate and very obvious party noises in the background. The sort you can buy on a pre-recorded tape to convince your wife you're not at your mistress's flat. Finally, with delayed reaction, Jay's voice came on the line.

'Hi . . . this is Jay.' He spoke as if he had trouble remembering his name.

'Ivo here . . . just wondering what you were up to.'

'Well, look . . . things are really cool here . . . I've got a few people round and we're just having a game of *Sexual Trivia*. Why don't you come over?'

He hesitated a second. 'No thanks, I'll give it a miss. But make sure you get your ass into my office tomorrow morning. It's time you earned that salary I pay you.'

Ivo left the office and got his chauffeur to drive back to his house in St James's via Shaftesbury Avenue and Piccadilly Circus. He gazed out of the window at the passing array of coloured neon, young Scandinavian tourists and mountains of Macdonald's wrappers. Every now and then they would pass an alley or a darkened doorway with a young girl standing in it, waiting. And each time, Ivo told the chauffeur to slow down. Just in case he spotted one with tufty hair and a stroppy expression.

Four

On the morning that Leofred was due to fly to Los Angeles, he was woken by a phone call from the travel agent.

'Hello, Mr Sammy here, Jingo Travel. I'm afraid I have some . . . some not very good news for you.'

'News?' Leofred tried to focus his sleepy brain.

'Yes, I am sorry sir, but Nightmair has gone bankrupt.'

Leofred groaned.

'It happens sometimes, with charter companies,' said Mr Sammy cheerfully. 'But never mind, you will go to Los Angeles. For an extra fifty pounds – cash – we can get you a very special deal.'

Several hours later, Leofred found himself on a Bangladeshi Airways flight to Los Angeles, via Amsterdam, Baghdad and Honolulu.

On his right was the fattest woman in the world. Her arm billowed over the arm rest onto his lunch tray, and her thigh spilled over onto his seat. On his left was a man who ordered a double scotch at half-hour intervals, lit up a new cigarette as soon as the old one was finished and proceeded to regale Leofred in a very boring voice with anecdotes on every single airline he had ever flown on. The woman in front went to sleep as soon as the plane took off, pushing her seat back to its furthest point so that it rested on Leofred's knee-caps, with the head-rest just touching his jaw-bone. Her baby leaned over the top of the row of seats and dribbled his pre-packed orange juice onto Leofred's thighs, crowing loudly with delight. Behind him, packed into three seats, was a Bangladeshi couple with four small children, all of whom screeched incessantly.

Leofred took the only course open to him. He paid the ten dollar charge for one of the plastic head-sets that give the wearer chronic ear-ache, and plugged into Channel 10 – *Sounds Eazi – middle-of-the-road melodies to spirit your tensions away*. Channel 3 – *Classical Chartbusters* and Channel 5 – *Thigh-slappin' Humour* were out of order.

After the plane had taken off and landed what seemed like countless times, there was a loud creaking, and a rickety screen was winched down from the ceiling. Several abortive starts later, the main feature was screened. It was a 1960s B movie called *Quest for Love*, starring Joan Collins as a fresh-faced air stewardess who doesn't know she's due to die in six short days and a hero in sideburns and turtleneck sweaters who does, because he knew her in another life.

Leofred followed the plot with difficulty for the first few minutes as he searched for Channel 6 – *Film Soundtrack*. When he found it, things did not become a lot clearer, as the dialogue on the headphones was about two lines behind what Joan and her groovy hunk were mouthing on the screen. Leofred watched through drooping eyelids until the point when our Joanie was being spirited away in an ambulance on a life-or-death mercy dash, then he fell into a shallow, cramped doze.

He missed the reputedly spectacular descent into Los Angeles International airport, thirty-six hours after leaving London. Instead he found himself staggering with bent knees around a garishly lit terminal building. Escalators slid up and down in every direction, elevators took people up and down to unimaginable destinations. Leofred stood there, blinking, cold in the air-conditioning, wondering which of the vast circular machines housed his luggage.

The next stage of the journey was going to be difficult, because he didn't know where he was going. He hadn't planned this far. It seemed that the centre of the city was about fifty miles away and a taxi ride would have cost most of his spending money. He went and queued for a bus.

'I'm going to Hollywood,' he said firmly.

The driver laughed. 'Ain't no buses go to Hollywood. Santa Monica's as far as I go. That's near enough.'

Leofred was prepared to believe him. He was too tired to argue, anyway. He sat in the bus in solitary splendour and was driven to Santa Monica. There were no other passengers. You didn't take buses in Los Angeles apparently, unless you belonged to an ethnic minority or were an old age pensioner. You had a vast tank of a car and you drove.

He found himself on the Pacific Highway on the edge of a steep, palm-fringed drop to a beach that went on forever. A faint, yellow haze hung in the air. He supposed it must be smog. He headed inland a few blocks and began to search for somewhere to stay. People stared at him as they drove past in their convertibles. The only other pedestrians he saw were a pair of nuns wearing sunglasses.

Eventually he found a cheap motel just off Arizona Boulevard, a pink, one-storey Spanish style building. It had an ancient and noisy air-conditioning system and a view over an outdoor kindergarten where the young of West Los Angeles were learning self-awareness and assertiveness techniques as they played in the dirt. The room had a television set and a courtesy video of goldfish swimming in a bowl, that lasted for a whole ninety minutes. It was very soothing.

Leofred switched it to 'Play' and instantly fell into an oblivious sleep.

He woke several hours later with a dry mouth, unable to remember where he was. It was hot, and in the brilliant sunlight that streamed through the shutters, his body looked as grey as an uncooked prawn. It was time to go to the beach and acquire a golden tan, or no-one would employ him for fear he had AIDs or some other wasting disease. Also, he was hungry. Perhaps he'd be able to get an ice-cream.

There were no ice-cream vendors to be found on Santa Monica Beach, but there was an establishment called 'Patrick's Roadhouse'. It was a rough and ready shack with red gingham-covered tables, filled with a strong smell of frying and not a lettuce leaf or an alfalfa sprout in sight. The eponymous Patrick was a fat pseudo-Irishman who was rude to the customers to give the place a sort of off-beat charm, an inverted chic, but who only succeeded in being offensive.

Leofred sat down on a bar stool and instantly had a glass of iced water slammed down in front of him.

'Yeah? You eating, or you just staring?'

'I'll . . . um . . . I'll have some waffles and some bacon. Please.' He knew from the Macdonalds commercial that was what Americans ate for breakfast.

'We don't have waffles. You can have bacon and egg.'

Patrick shouted something incomprehensible at a Mexican woman in the back, and the smell of frying intensified.

'So . . . you're English, huh? I can tell from that ugly colour you got.'

Leofred nodded and turned his attention back to the iced water.

'What's the matter – don't wanna talk? Not good enough for you, are we?'

63

Before he could reply, Patrick had slammed the plate of food in front of him and flounced away, or at least, done the best impression of flouncing that a fat person could muster.

Leofred did not feel like eating bacon and eggs, especially not smothered with *salsa verde*, nor did he feel like being forced into conversation with Patrick, who was watching him like an over-fed hawk, waiting for him to complain about the food. He looked around for alternative conversation. Two young men sitting further along the bar returned his tentative smile.

'You're from the UK, aren't you, mon?' He was to learn that his accent would provide the opening gambit for practically every conversation he had in America. He didn't recognise the twang of the other men. Perhaps they were from the mid-West.

'You just got 'ere?'

He nodded.

'My name's Kevin and this here's Stuart. From Soonderland. We've just got 'ere an' all. Yisterday.'

Leofred made the appropriate signs of recognition.

'Greeat here, isn't it? We're having a greeat time, aren't we, Stu?'

'Yup,' said Stuart, swigging on his tequila. 'We've just doon one o' them guided coach tours of the Universal Studios. Bloody brilliant, mon! Magic!'

Patrick was eyeing them belligerently, as though a colonial conspiracy was brewing. Fortunately at that moment another man strolled over to join them, and he was unmistakeably Californian. Yellow blond hair standing on end in a long crew cut, sawn-off jeans that Leofred thought everyone had abandoned in the seventies and a heavy gold medallion thumping against his chocolate brown chest.

'*Hi!*' He gave the word as much stress as a one syllable

64

word could possibly cope with. 'Chet Daytona. How're you doing?' He thrust his hand at Leofred's and began wringing it. 'Say, that's a great accent you got there, you oughta use it.'

Chet ignored the other two, presumably he couldn't understand what they were saying. 'You gotta nagent?'

'Er . . . not yet.'

'That's great, 'cause I know just the guy. Randy Promo. Deals with all the big studios. I just happen to have his card here – '

He fished into the front left pocket of his skin-tight cut-offs, an operation that could have ruined his fertility for life.

' . . . and here's *my* business card.' There followed a repeat performance with the other pocket. The denim of his shorts creaked in protest.

Leofred stared at Randy Promo's card. '*Theatrical agent. Everglade Mansions, East Hollywood.*'

'Guess it doesn't mean much to you, huh? Tell you what, I'll drive you over there now. I'm heading that way.'

Leofred had no idea what – if anything – he would have to discuss with a theatrical agent, but before he knew it, he was sitting next to the barefoot Chet in his open-topped Volkswagen Beetle, driving down wide streets, away from the beach and up a steep canyon. There were girls in shorts and bikinis on all sides, some on roller skates, some on racing cycles, but none on foot.

'Here – ' Chet pulled a pair of reflecting shades out of the glove box. 'You better put these on.'

'Ah . . . it's all right actually, my eyes are okay, thank – '

'Put 'em on! People will think you're weird if you drive around in a convertible without wearing shades. You don't wanna look weird, do you?'

Leofred knew that he must already look weird. The tip of his nose was frying to a crisp, purpley red in the relentless smog-filtered sun.

65

They were driving down Hollywood Boulevard.

'Schlocksville,' observed Chet. It looked like a studio set, its cheap frontage cardboardy and sleazy. Here, the stars had left their imprint in cement. An old black bag-woman stood in Betty Grable's footsteps and waved her fists angrily, shouting. A group of muggers wandered around looking for someone to mug.

They parked outside one of the cardboard buildings and went up in the elevator.

'*Heyyyy!*' said Randy Promo when he saw Chet.

'*Heyyyy!*' responded Chet. They slapped palms.

'How're you doin', good buddy?'

'Good. And you?'

'Good.'

Leofred was to learn that the meaningless greeting ritual was as highly developed here as it was in certain circles in England, except there you said you were 'fine', here you were 'good'.

Randy Promo was like an older version of Chet, with a few streaks of grey in his brilliant gold hair and a few more medallions to prove he'd put in longer service as a Californian. He wore a mint-green polyester safari suit.

'So – you got yourself a great accent there, kid,' he said, sinking down behind a rather dusty chrome and glass desk, at sea in an ocean of grubby orange shag-pile. On the walls were framed photographs of identical-looking sets of teeth, grinning out from their various faces. Across them were scrawled '*To my best buddy Randy, a close personal friend, love Rock*' . . . '*To Randy, my love and gratitude always, Shirlee.*' The handwriting was identical on all of them.

'You bin in movies?' asked Randy.

'No.'

'On TV?'

'No.'

'Know how to act?'

'No.'

'Well, that doesn't matter so much . . . But listen, I can get you a great deal.' He punched some figures into a pocket calculator. 'I gotta small part on a daytime soap for someone with a classy accent. Six episode contract. Six hundred dollars an episode, that's three thousand six hundred bucks . . .'

Leofred couldn't believe his luck.

' . . . basic. Then you've got your national insurance deduction of around ten per cent, your union membership, the casting director's cut of twenty per cent . . . and then there's my fee . . . and tax. I figure that'll leave you with . . .' He punched in more numbers. ' . . . about thirty dollars an episode. You interested?'

Leofred smiled politely. 'I'm afraid I don't really think I could manage on that amount.'

Randy shook his head. 'Jeeez. You kids. You want the moon. Okay, okay, I can get you an extra in a douche commercial. How about it?'

'No, thank you. Perhaps . . . perhaps if I could start by reading some scripts – '

Randy laughed. 'Reading *scripts*! Where's that gonna get you, for Chrissakes? You're going to end up doing just what all the other hopefuls do, I just bet . . .'

Leofred had no idea what that was.

'You're goin' ta end up as a goddam parking jockey!'

Byron Ferberger, famous movie and TV producer, was sitting beside the swimming pool, beneath the baking-hot sun.

Surprisingly he was indoors at the time, on Lot 23 of the True Life film studios in Century City. He had had a pool constructed for him to sit and relax beside, and next to it an enormous circular UVA lamp had been erected, which would resemble the sun when it was switched on. He wore madras bermudas and shades, and every now and then he would snap his fingers at a secretary, who would step forward and rub more oil into his huge teak-coloured body.

Byron Ferberger was a busy man. At any one time he was producing several network shows and developing umpteen major motion picture features. He was also a powerful man.

'Get me my phone!' he shouted.

Two minions humped an enormous console onto the set, the size of a Hammond organ and covered in switches, keyboards and computer screens. This was Ferberger's telephone. To an accompaniment of flashing coloured lights and digital bleeps, he called his various agents and talent scouts around the world, and checked how his investments were moving on the London, New York and Tokyo exchanges.

'Okay, Mr Ferberger, we're ready to roll.'

Ferberger was on the set to watch the shooting of one of his productions, a daytime soap opera called *One Big Happy Family*. The director had been rehearsing a day player, who was earning six hundred dollars for saying one line. Now they were ready to shoot the scene, which was to run thus: Inside her condo, Shelley has just had a great shock. She has just been told by her lover, Noel, that he has been concealing the fact that he is gay. As the shock sinks in, Shelley's parents arrive to reveal the terrible truth that Noel is really her long-lost brother who was kidnapped twenty years earlier by a heartless fiend with a grudge against the family. Heartbroken Shelley has to reveal to her parents that their son is gay. At this point a delivery boy arrives, the role taken by the day player.

'We felt the scene needed it,' the assistant junior script editor explained to Ferberger. 'You know, here we are, in Shelley's apartment, and it's easy for the audience to forget that there is a world outside it, a city. We need to be reminded that real life is going on and, like, Shelley has forgotten in the tension of the moment that she's ordered this pizza. It gives the scene some bathos.'

'Great, love it,' said Ferberger, motioning to his secretary to turn the 'sun' up higher, 'let's go for it.'

The actors were given their markers, the sound and lighting checked. A few drops of glycerine were added to Shelley's otherwise immaculately made-up face. On the other side of the cardboard door to the 'apartment', the young day player shifted from foot to foot nervously, mouthing his one line over and over.

'Okay, quiet on set please . . . *and* . . . action!'

'Noel,' sobbed Shelley, dabbing her eyes and moving away from a powder blue sofa to a lone rubber plant. 'How can you have done this to me? Lied to me . . . deceived me . . . and I *trusted* you!' She burst into realistic sobs.

'*Great!*' murmured the director from the edge of the sound stage, 'Great, Kelly.' Kelly was the actress who played Shelley.

'But baby . . .' Noel; lean, square-jawed, with expensive taste, left the sofa and followed Shelley to the rubber plant. 'It don't mean that I don't love you! I do, you know that!'

Noel tried to put his arms around Shelley, but she pulled away and went back to the blue sofa. Soon the sofa was crowded, as the sound engineer gave the signal for an electronic door chime and Shelley's parents, made up to look grey and shocked, joined in the recriminations and explanations.

'Oh, honey,' said Shelley's grief-stricken mother, following Shelley over to the rubber plant. 'If only we coulda known. If only we coulda spared you the heartache!'

'That's right, honey . . .' Shelley's father paced towards the plant. Noel went back to the sofa. 'We never woulda kept the truth from you, you know that.'

'But Momma, Poppa,' said the sobbing Shelley. 'There's something you don't know. You see, Noel is – '

'*Ding-dong!*'

'Who the hell can that be?' An agitated Noel decamped to the rubber plant. Shelley's parents sat down on the sofa.

Shelley flung open the cardboard door.

Silence.

The day player proffered an empty box. 'Er . . .'

'CUT!' screamed the director.

'Gee, I guess I just forgot the line. Just slipped clean out of my head.'

'Okay, we'll take it again. From "*Who the hell can that be?*" . . .'

This time Shelley wrenched the door so hard it nearly left its hinges. The day player was so surprised, he dropped the box.

'CUT! take three and . . . *action!*'

'Er . . . here's the delivery you wanted, ma'am.'

'CUT! It's "*I'm delivering the pizza you ordered, ma'am.*" You're supposed to have learned the goddam line! Okay, once more please. Take four . . .'

'Ma'am . . . this is the pizza – '

'CUT!!'

'What the hell is going on here?' hissed Byron to one of the assistant directors. 'They're supposed to have been rehearsed.'

'You know how it is with these one-line johnnies, Byron. They only know they're on a coupla hours before shooting and they get nervous.'

After seventeen failed takes, the delivery man was safely relieved of his pizza.

'Thank Christ, it's a wrap,' sighed Ferberger.

But it wasn't, not quite. Various men had started tramping to and fro across the set, pointing to the powder-blue sofa and the rubber plant and arguing. The beleaguered director, who had aged ten years since the start of shooting, was waving his arms in despair.

'*Now* what the hell do we have here?' Ferberger was starting to get annoyed himself. 'Surely not? – '

The assistant director nodded and sighed. 'Looks like. Seems it was that goddam plant.'

One of the technicians' unions had just gone on strike, because earlier that day an unauthorised person had moved the rubber plant from its original position next to the sofa. Shooting would be cancelled for the whole day while the dispute was settled.

Byron Ferberger swung into action. After all, what was the point of unlimited wealth and power if you didn't use it? He telephoned the union head office and made a generous donation to their funds. Shooting was on again.

Byron sighed, removed his sunglasses and lay back for a few minutes to soak up the 'sun'.

'Call for you, Mr Ferberger.'

'Hi, Byron! Nik Warlock here. How ya doing?'

'Good, and you?'

'Good. Listen, I've got this great idea going.' Nik Warlock was an up-and-coming screen writer. 'Why don't we take some of the great classics and give them a contemporary, American feel. Like Rambo in period dress. Have a guy who goes round settling scores and wiping out the bad guys dressed in Civil War costume, that kind of thing. Reckon we could get Sly Stallone interested.'

'Great, let's talk about it sometime.'

Byron hung up and closed his eyes, only to be interrupted again, this time by a journalist from *Celebrity* magazine.

'Mr Ferberger, here are the proofs from that four-page feature we're running. The editor said you got to check them out before we run it.'

He squinted at a photograph of himself in the position

he was in now, stretched out on a lounger beside the pool. 'You can't run this picture.'

'But Mr Ferberger – '

'Haven't you guys ever heard of touching up? I mean – look at my piece!' He stabbed a fat finger at the image on the page. 'It looks like an orange possum is sitting on toppa my head! I paid five thousand bucks to have them match it up exactly with my own hair colour. In your picture the colour's totally different!'

'Okay, Mr Ferberger, we'll get it airbrushed.'

'No! I don't want that picture at all, ya hear me? I don't look serious enough. I wanna shot of me wearing a velvet smoking jacket and reading the works of William Shakespeare.'

'Okay, Mr Ferberger.'

'And how about some shots of me with my family? After all, my latest TV hit is called *One Big Happy Family*. You got yourselves an ideal hook there. What the public want to see is a shot of me with my own happy family.'

When *Celebrity* magazine called to fix an appointment for the photo shoot, Cherie Ferberger was talking to her interior decorator.

'We're gonna haveta take my new look into account, Alvin,' she said plaintively to the young man who wore gold leather top-siders and an earring to match.

'You got it, Mrs F.'

'The thing is, I'm having my hair frosted with a new shade that Giorgio just *swears* I gotta try, and that means I gotta raid Rodeo Drive for a whole lotta new outfits, and *that* means I gotta fix up the house to match.'

Alvin made sympathetic clucking noises as he went round the room, scribbling notes in a gold leather Organofax. 'I quite agree,' he drawled. Alvin was from Buffalo, but he affected the twang of the deep South, thinking it made him more interesting. 'Peach was last year's colour, but now you should just *die* to have peach in your house. This season's shade is quite definitely lilac.'

He pronounced it 'lie-lack' with syllables.

'That's what Giorgio said,' sighed Cherie. Personally, she had invested a lot in peach. The drapes, the carpets, the dried flower arrangements, the oil paintings. (That *had* been hard, finding original Impressionist works that were predominantly peach-toned.) The pool had been re-tiled in peach and white ceramics. Her Pontiac Firebird had been resprayed. Even the borzoi had a peach rinse.

Cherie made a big fuss about all the refurbishing that had to be done, but in fact there was no other way for her to pass the time. She was a Hollywood Housewife, and as such her raison d'être was to spend her husband's cash as fast as possible. A great deal of it was devoted to the cause of Keeping Cherie Beautiful. She was forty-five, but looked thirty. Her face had been tucked, ironed and pinned, and then regularly ex-foliated, electrolysed and aromatised. She'd had an eyebrow and eyelash transplant. The hair on her legs had been permanently removed, a process that had taken years to complete. Only the very dedicated went to such lengths.

'Oh my God, Alvin,' she sighed, tripping across the lounge in her high-heeled mules. 'What a life I have! How many women suffer the pressures I suffer? Isn't it bad enough that I have to have my husband's senile mother and unmanageable daughter living in the house with me?'

'Y'all do have a problem,' sighed the ever-sympathetic Alvin, who had his calculator secreted in the palm of his hand and was working out how he could bump up his enormous commission. 'Meanwhile, think lie-lack.'

Thinking lilac thoughts that were going to cost her

husband thousands of dollars, Cherie went into the bath-room to get ready to go to the beauty parlour. This was a time-consuming and somewhat contradictory process, like the English obsession with tidying up before the charlady arrives.

'Let me see . . .' Cherie licked her lips. 'What shall I go for? I know – beige.'

She reached for a console on the dresser and pressed a button marked 'Beige'. The wardrobe doors opened auto-matically and out slid an entire section for Cherie's perusal. It contained beige blouses, beige slacks, beige sweaters. Another panel opened up in the vanity unit and offered her a choice of cosmetics that toned with beige.

She selected an outfit and slipped out of the clothes that she was wearing. 'Hey girl, you've got a *great* body!' she murmured to her reflection, running her hands over her perfectly constructed breasts, her taut belly, her slender hips.

The door opened and Carla, the maid, came into the room. She was a six-foot Jamaican with a figure that left Carla's for dead. Cherie insisted that Carla wear a frumpy black uniform. Carla hated Cherie.

'What is it, Carla?' snapped Cherie, sitting down on the stool and running a brush quickly through the streaky peach-frosted hair that was soon to be taken care of by Giorgio's knowing fingers.

'It's my brother, Tyrone, ma'am. My folks are trying to put him through college and I want to help out some.'

'If you're trying for a raise, forget it.'

'Oh, but I don't think I will, ma'am,' said Carla in the same soft, respectful, entirely sinister tone. 'Because you see, I found something of yours, ma'am. When you asked me to put the bills on your desk. See, I found your birth certificate.'

Cherie made a little, exasperated noise. 'If that's all Carla, why, it's hardly a sin to tell *Celebrity* magazine you're thirty-nine when you're forty-five. Not when you're in great shape.'

'Not that birth certificate. The other one.'

Cherie stopped brushing.

'Yes, ma'am. You see, now I know that you weren't really Cherie Landers before you married Mr Ferberger. I know that you were really Raymond Milano until that clever doctor fixed you up with tits an' a pussy.'

Cherie's shoulders slumped. 'So you're blackmailing me,' she said, her voice suddenly gruff. 'Is that all?'

She had known it would happen sooner or later. After all, this was Hollywood.

Four hours later, Cherie drove back to Bel Air with Melodie, Byron's daughter from his third marriage.

Cherie and Melodie hated each other, but that didn't stop them from going to the beauty parlour together. They each hoped to be present when the other suffered a really disastrous haircut, or the beautician got the depilatory wax too hot.

'D'ya think I should have another nose job?' Melodie asked through her blueberry chewing gum. 'I think I should have another nose job. The last one didn't work too good.'

Cherie squinted at her step-daughter in the driving mirror. 'It's fine, honey . . .'

. . . *And why bother with such details when the rest of you's a walking disaster?*

Melodie was twenty-two, an aspiring actress and Valley Girl. She looked like a pig wearing a blonde hair-piece. Before her nose job she looked like a Jewish pig wearing a blonde hairpiece. She was short and narrow-shouldered; wide everywhere else. Cherie once remarked to one of her girlfriends that when Melodie walked into a room, her ass was still coming through the door five minutes later.

'I should concentrate on getting rid of your tooth brace,' she said.

And forget about the rest, it's a lost cause . . .

'What're you and Daddy doing tonight?'

'I'm going to a baby shower,' lied Cherie, who had an extra-curricular appointment with her tennis coach.

'Eugh – who's had a baby?'

'Er, Darlene,' said Cherie quickly.

'But she's at least forty! Gross me *out*! I'm *never* going to have a baby. It *kills* your figure!'

What figure, you little . . . But Cherie was in no mood to pick a fight with Melodie. She was thinking about Carla's surprise revelation. She'd given Carla the twenty grand, and now she was going to have to get it back from Byron.

Melodie didn't really feel like picking a fight with her stepmother. She was thinking about her father. It was about time he did something to further her career, she decided.

The peach Pontiac slid through the electronic gates and into the garage. Cherie and Melodie both went inside and lay in wait for Byron.

Cherie got to him first.

'Hi, honey,' she murmured, kissing him on the shoulder as he climbed out of the shower. Her lips slid off him. He used up so much sun-tan oil in the average day that he had the feel of a wet sea-lion. 'How was your day?'

'What the fuck's going on out there?' he demanded, pointing out of the window at the swimming pool. Several men were at work with drills and excavators.

'What? Oh, that's nothing, honey. They're just replacing the peach tiles with lilac ones.'

Byron grunted.

' . . . and I need twenty thousand dollars.'

'No way! I give you enough already. The answer's no.'

'Ah, but it's gonna be "yes" . . . by the way, Byron, don't you love this new lilac frosting? Giorgio's a genius . . . you see, darlin', I know one or two little things. That you lied to George Stetson about the budget for *Big Smoke* so that you could underpay him . . . that while the shooting was delayed on your last picture, the entire budget was sitting in your off-shore account and you were pocketing the interest . . .'

Byron pulled a roll of thousand-dollar bills from his shorts and tossed them at her. 'Okay, bitch, take twenty.'

'Did I say twenty?' purred Cherie, 'Oh honey, what I meant was fifty.'

Melodie sat in the kitchen, drinking a peanut butter and malt triple shake. The straw made a loud whining noise as she sucked through her metal braces, like a dental drill.

She was watching Carla as she shimmied around the kitchen with Walkman headphones on, preparing supper. She hated Carla. Carla's long, shapely legs made hers look like sausages. Worst of all, she hadn't even gone to a plastic surgeon for them. And she was far too uppity for a maid.

But just this once Melodie kept silent. Carla was about to be useful to her.

She heard her father go outside to argue with the men who were fixing the pool.

'*Daddy!*' she whined, 'Daddy, I wanna talk to you.'

Byron was stretched out on a lounger. Melodie was about to sit on his lap, but she decided she didn't want to risk giving him a hernia. Instead she affected a cutesy lisp.

'Does Daddy love his little Mellie?'

77

'Yes,' sighed Byron, without opening his eyes.

'Enough to create her very own little soap opera for her?'

'No, not that much.'

Melodie's voice dropped to its normal pitch. 'In that case – get this. I saw you and Carla making out the other day. And I'm going to tell Cherie.'

Byron opened his eyes. 'You – '

'I was looking through the picture windows and I saw the two of you in the jacuzzi. At least, I saw your head and her black ass. And the five hundred dollar bill you slipped her. And I took some real bitchin' shots with that new Polaroid camera you gave me.'

Byron sighed noisily. 'Fer Chrissakes – '

'So you better do it, Daddy. You better get me that show. Because I wanna be a star!'

Five

'Can't we go out? I want to go out.'

Heidi was lying on her bed in Grafton Road and Charles Jolyon was lying on top of her.

'I thought we were having rather a nice time staying in,' murmured Charles; he used his weight to pinion her as he groped around and tried to enter her again. Heidi did not offer any assistance. She was angry with him. She lay still for a while as he pounded away on top of her, then decided to call a halt to the proceedings. Charles was a greedy and voracious lover, and if he wanted to he could go on all night. She could wake up at five o'clock in the morning and find herself impaled, with him breathing away heavily behind her.

Their relationship seemed to have fallen into a pattern. If a fiasco occurred and Charles was prevented from attending a rendezvous, then he was always shrewd enough to consolidate his position quickly. He would rush around to her flat as soon as possible and impress on her that he really cared, by pressing on her hard for several hours. This was one such occasion, but Heidi was still unforgiving.

'I want to go out.' she repeated. 'We never go out anywhere in the evening.'

'We can't!' Charles groaned into her shoulder, 'Someone might see us.'

'And tell your wife?' sneered Heidi. 'Is that what you're scared of? Why does she keep having to go out in the evenings anyway?' She pushed Charles to one side so that they lay facing one another. 'Aren't you suspicious?'

'What do you mean?'

Heidi emitted an exaggerated sigh of impatience. 'I *mean* dummy, is she having an affair?'

'God, I don't know! How does one tell?'

Heidi knew how to tell if a single girl was having an affair. She wore her make-up to bed, only removing it the next morning after *he* had gone. All those tell-tale mascara stains on the pillowcase. And she had her bikini line waxed when she wasn't going away on holiday. She wasn't sure about married women, though. The rules were different and so, presumably, were the outward signs.

But she'd had more than enough of thinking about Charles' wife.

'*I'm* going out!' she announced, 'Even if you're not!'

She jumped off the bed and climbed into a pair of polka dot pedal-pushers and an orange vest. 'Are you coming?'

Charles groaned and rolled over, his body looking somewhat ridiculous now that he was the only naked person in the room.

Heidi went out, leaving him. She just intended to walk, to wander around in the night and let her anger evaporate. If she wasn't gone long, then perhaps Charles would still be there when she came back. She considered this, then set the situation up in her mind like a little test. She would see how much he cared. If she came back and he had waited for her, then she would know he cared a lot.

Distances seem to be covered quicker at night than by day, and in no time at all, Heidi was at the tube station, then rattling her way south on the Bakerloo line. She got off at Oxford Circus and walked towards Tottenham Court Road. There were still hordes of people about, mostly young boys in white socks and grey slip-ons, their designer logos competing with their gold chains and signet rings.

A car screeched to a halt at the kerb, quadrophonic speakers blaring.

'Hi!' said a voice, 'You're Hettie, right?'

'Heidi.' she said coldly.

'Sorry, I'm terrible with names. I'm Jay Cathcart – we met the other day.

'I remember.'

'Well, nice to see you again! What are you doing?'

Heidi flung a withering look through the open roof of the Twin Cam Turbo-charged Intercooler. 'I'm soliciting. I'm a hooker in my spare time.'

Jay stared back at her and so did the dumb-looking blonde sitting beside him. ' . . . Oh, I get it, it's a joke. Hey, that's cool. Listen, we're going to the Bao-Wow. Why don't you come?'

Heidi nodded and climbed into the back of the car. She was curious about the Bao-Wow Club, whose name was whispered with awe by the trendier secretaries at TV Mayhem. Besides, this would *really* test Charles.

'This is Sasha,' said Jay, taking both hands off the wheel and narrowly missing an elderly couple at a zebra crossing. 'Hey, two OAPs with one blow – score one hundred points!'

Jay and Sasha laughed hysterically. Heidi wondered what had happened to the girl he was with at the Basmati Brasserie. Perhaps he didn't have a steady girlfriend. It seemed unlikely anyone would put up with him.

The awfulness of the Bao-Wow Club fascinated her. It was packed with Jay and Sasha lookalikes, swaying nonchalantly to songs that were hits before most of them were born and using conversation simply as a vehicle to prove how hip and aware they were. Snippets of it floated around Heidi:

' . . . D'you know what "virement" means? It's a really

"in" word, apparently. But it's not in the Shorter Oxford . . .'

' . . . Yah, being freelance used to give me major financial hassles. So I said "no way" . . .'

' . . . We've all started going to White City on Tuesday nights to watch the dogs. Really fun thing to do. Real scream . . .'

' . . . Isn't it something to do with the environment? . . .'

' . . . so then we went to this really great promo party at the Stuff Hyperstore in Oxford Street. Bob and Paula were there . . .'

' . . . He's doing a piece for *Harper's* on celebrities' favourite launderettes . . .'

A tall young man with thickly gelled hair wafted up to Heidi. 'Hi, didn't I see you at Flora's last week?' As he spoke, he looked over her shoulder and into the middle distance.

'No.'

'Hey, excuse me, there's someone over there I have to talk to . . .' He mouthed *'Hi, darling!'* at some invisible person. 'Got to run. Are you going to Rosie's party next week?'

Heidi shook her head.

'Great – see you there.'

He dematerialised. Heidi went to find Jay. 'I'm leaving,' she told him. 'I've had enough of this place.'

'Okay, I'll give you a lift.'

She was surprised. 'What about Sasha?'

Jay shrugged. 'She's gone AWOL.'

Heidi got into Jay's car while he busied himself clearing the windscreen of parking tickets and throwing them in a nearby dustbin.

'Wanna come back and watch a video?'

She hesitated. 'Can I just make a phone call first?'

'Sure.' Jay switched on the ignition and handed her his car-phone.

Heidi punched in her own number, trying to remember whether she'd switched on her answering machine. She hadn't. The phone rang and rang. Charles may be asleep, she thought. She let it go on ringing, ignoring Jay's quizzical glances.

He wasn't there.

'Let's go and watch that video,' she said.

'This is one of my all-time favourite films!' Jay rubbed his hands as he programmed the little black box.

Heidi stretched out on the minimalist grey sofa with a can of beer and prepared mentally for *Driller Killer From the Grave III*, but was confronted instead with Julie Andrews looking as though polyunsaturated margarine wouldn't melt in her mouth, singing '*Feed the birds, tuppence a beahg, tuppence, tuppence, tuppence a beahg*.'

'*Mary Poppins*,' said Jay, 'Great movie!'

He obviously wasn't about to seduce her. Heidi was relieved. She couldn't help liking him though. There was something very straightforward about so much pretentiousness.

'What did you think of the Bao-Wow?' he asked, lighting a black Balkan Sobranie.

'A lot of affected crap.'

To her surprise, Jay smiled. 'You know,' he said grudgingly, 'when I first met you, I thought – ' He made a rocking motion with his hand that indicated 'merely so-so', ' . . . but you know something, you're really cool.'

'Thank you.'

'How are you getting on with my big brother?'

'I'm not.'

'But you've still got to work with him?'

'First interview tomorrow morning.'

'He can be a mighty pain.' Jay sighed sympathetically.

83

'He wants to buy me.'

'But you're not for sale, right?' A knowing smirk crossed Jay's face. 'Let me tell you, they all say that. But how do you think he got to be so rich? By not taking no for an answer, that's how. He'll get you in the end, and I for one, can't wait to see the feathers fly!'

Heidi buried her head under a cushion. 'Piss off Jay!'

A hundred thousand! Half a million . . . okay, a million. A million. It's worth it to me if you'll just –

'I'd like to get straight on with this thing, okay?' Heidi switched on her tape-recorder and slammed it down on Ivo Cathcart's massive desk. She was chewing a piece of gum, rolling it around with her teeth and making unfeminine slurping noises. 'Okay, talk.'

'What do you want?'

'Anything, I don't care.' Heidi slung one leg over the arm of her chair. 'Start with your early childhood.'

Ivo started talking about formative experiences at nursery school when he had bought a job lot of sherbet fountains and sold them off at a profit. But he wasn't really listening to his own voice, or thinking about what he was saying. He was quivering with desire. It was only with great difficulty that he restrained himself from jumping up and racing around the room. She made him feel charged with energy.

He pretended to look at the tape-recorder, but really his eyes were on Heidi. She was wearing tight jeans and stubby little yellow sneakers. Her mousy hair stuck up briskly, her nails were bitten back so far that they had almost disappeared. Yet for Ivo she was the stuff of fantasy. He loved her off-hand, careless style of speech and posture. He loved the sloppy way she scuffed her feet as she walked. He would, yes at that moment he really would, have given a million pounds to see her dressed up in a tight pencil skirt and black stockings; her short square feet crammed into patent leather stilettos. Or just to glimpse her in her natural habitat. She probably wore a balding terrycloth bathrobe that was too short over her backside . . . and bedsocks. Battered little sheepskin moccasins. The thought of it was like a physical thirst.

'Hang on a minute . . .' Heidi flipped out of the chair. 'Got to turn the tape over.'

She hadn't really been listening to what Ivo was saying, either, but she was thinking about him. He had a power that had nothing to do with charm. He was completely in control of his environment. Machines worked for him. His lighter always lit first time. He never dropped or fumbled with things. No movement was wasted; he conserved energy. These were qualities so alien to Heidi that she couldn't prevent a glimmer of admiration. But he was still a total bastard and she didn't know why on earth she was sitting there opposite him.

Heidi was having one of her periodic 'My Life's a Mess' days. She felt like scrubbing everything off the slate and starting again. Here she was, being forced to do a job she didn't want to do and there wasn't even any sympathy to go home to in the evenings. Poor Charles didn't seem to find it any easier to resolve his domestic situation, and as a result they never seemed to get anywhere. She needed to get away. She needed to do what Leofred had done, and escape. A postcard from him had arrived that morning, and the sight of the sea and the palm trees was enough to make her howl with despair, even if they *were* all plastic.

'Okay, that's it. Your time's up. We'll do some more next week.' Heidi jumped up and switched off the tape recorder.

'But I haven't finished what I was saying!' Ivo protested angrily.

'Tough. I've got to go.' She snatched up the tape-recorder. Ivo's hand came down, just in time to stop her. There was a tussle.

'Dinner – tonight,' he said, 'We can eat anywhere you like in the whole of London. Langan's, Le Gavroche, La Caprice . . . Just give me your address.'

Look, Pig-Face . . .

'Look, Pig-Face,' she found herself saying before she could disengage her mouth from her brain. The object in question went an even deeper shade of bacon. 'Forget it!'

She stuffed the tape-recorder into her little wicker-basket and stomped out, failing to notice the postcard that fluttered out as she crammed in the lead and adaptor.

Ivo noticed everything. After she had gone, he picked it up. It was a touched-up photograph of Venice Beach, California, featuring a lot of sun-tanned bodies.

'Dear Heid, Arrived safely. Weather good, if a bit hot. Found a job straightaway. Hope you're OK. Love, Leof.'

Ivo smiled. If it was from her lover, she couldn't have picked a less articulate and imaginative one. But it wasn't the message he was interested in.

'Miss H. Plunkett, 201 Grafton Road, Queen's Park . . .'

He grinned. He always got what he wanted. Somehow.

The sender of the postcard was at that moment just finishing his day's work.

It was two in the morning and Leofred felt as though he had been driving all day. He climbed wearily from behind the steering wheel, smoothed down his red crimplene uniform jacket and straightened his bow-tie. Then he handed the car keys to the waiting owner.

'There ya go,' he said in what he hoped was a passable American accent. 'Have a nice day!'

He had learned during his brief employment as a parking jockey at the Tequila Cantina that it was best not to reveal his English origins. The customers always wanted to talk to him about it, which kept everyone else waiting and the boss got annoyed.

'Just one more,' said the manager, handing him another set of keys, 'Then you can go home.' He pointed to a fat aquamarine Rolls Royce Corniche with the registration BTF 1. ' . . . *And careful with the motherfucker!*' he hissed.

Leofred climbed gingerly into the cockpit and groped around for the controls. It was dark in the parking lot and he couldn't see the markings on the gear stick that indicated where reverse was. He *thought* he was in reverse, but the wheels rolled briskly forward. There was a loud crunching noise and the sound of splintering headlamp glass. He still couldn't see anything.

Then, through the darkness, the furious owner loomed into view.

'What the fuck are you doing?!' yelled Byron T. Ferberger.

In his confusion, Leofred forgot to be American. 'Oh God, I'm frightfully sorry, sir I – '

'Hey, you got an English accent! That's great! . . .'

Leofred covered his face with his hands and groaned.

' . . . You interested in doing some acting?'

Twelve hours later, and several thousand miles away, Ivo Cathcart's white Bentley Continental was turning into Grafton Road.

'Stop here!' he told the driver, 'I want to walk . . .'

' . . . *Shit!*' he said to himself five minutes later, 'This bloody road goes on forever.'

Eventually he found number two-hundred-and-one, and

marvelled at its shabbiness. It aroused him, like everything else about Heidi. He did not ring on the doorbell, or knock at the door. He had no intention of going in. He simply wanted to look, and to fantasise.

There was a light on in a top floor room, and the purple curtains were open. I bet she lives up there in a bed-sit, thought Ivo, and I bet it's really squalid. With empty baked bean cans lying around. He hoped so. And when she had friends around, they probably drank wine out of toothmugs. She probably used words like 'willy' and 'wee' instead of 'prick' and 'piss'. Perhaps she even left her dirty underwear lying around on the floor.

He wanted to pick it up and sniff at it like a dog, to wallow around in her sexuality, to paw her amongst her teddy bears and stuffed animals. He wanted to leave sticky stains all over the sheets on her narrow single bed. Most of all he wanted *her*, he just wanted her.

Two hours later, when the curtains were hurriedly pulled to and the light switched off. Ivo was still standing there under the streetlamp.

Six

Heidi stormed into Mike Marshall's office at TV Mayhem.

'I want to be taken off this Cathcart job!'

Mike took off his new fuchsia pink spectacles and rubbed his brow wearily. 'Heidi, Heidi . . . Ivo Cathcart has *asked* to have you on the job. How can I take you off? We'll lose the contract.'

'I'll tell you *how*!' said Heidi, '*Fast*, is how. Because if I don't get away from that man soon, I'm going to commit grievous bodily harm, or possibly murder. And then you really *will* lose the contract!'

'Please, Heidi. Please,' Mike adopted his embattled supremo expression, 'Just tell me exactly what it is you have against the man.'

'He's trying to buy me!' snarled Heidi, 'Exactly as if I were a frozen chicken, or a sack of potatoes. Just look at this – '

She brandished an envelope addressed to 'H. Plunkett, 201 Grafton Road, London NW'. Inside it was a cheque for a million pounds, made payable to her and signed 'I. Cathcart'.

Mike stared at it, wishing he were a girl of twenty-four. 'I see what you mean.'

'I want *out*, Mike. And that means as far away as possible!'

Heidi hurled herself out of Mike's office and straight into the arms of Charles. He was carrying a sheaf of important looking papers so that if anyone saw him they would think he was in the middle of something urgent. In fact he was wandering the corridors in search of Heidi.

'Heidi, great! Listen, I've got something incredibly important to – '

'And I don't want to talk to *you* either!'

She ran past the huge, smiling celebrity blow-ups, through reception and into the street. She had agreed to meet Jay for lunch, and although she wasn't sure she was in the mood for him, at least it gave her an excuse to put the twin udders of TV Mayhem as far behind her as possible.

Jay breezed into the restaurant a fashionable ten minutes late, tanned, relaxed and smiling.

'Heyy, what's going down, kid, *que pasa?*'

'You're a jerk, Jay.'

'I know.'

That was the thing about Jay. He enjoyed being a jerk. He exploited it. He was *good* at it.

'This is Daisy,' he said, pointing to the identikit blonde at his side. He didn't apologise for bringing someone along to their luncheon *à deux* or offer any explanation. There wasn't really any need to. Heidi had never seen Jay with the same girl twice, and yet they were all exactly the same. He neither seemed to know, nor to care much about them, and they were usually 'shed' somehow during the proceedings. Heidi took no more notice than if Jay had brought along a piece of hand luggage.

'Heidi, you look like you need an afternoon off,' he said after lunch. 'Or better still, a month. Why don't we go for a joy ride?'

'Don't you have to get back?'

'Back?'

'To your office.'

Jay laughed. 'Of course not. What are secretaries for?'

'Jay, what exactly do you *do*?' asked Heidi as the two of them climbed into the car. Daisy, inevitably, had been shed.

'I work for my brother.'

'But I've never seen you actually do any *work*.'

'Well . . . it's not work as such. I'm in charge of Rapier's Far Eastern operations.' He shoved Bruce Springsteen into the in-car compact disc player and began to chant along tunelessly. '*Born* in the USA, *born* in the USA . . .'

'What are Rapier's Far Eastern operations?'

Jay shrugged. 'I've no idea.'

They left London on the A2, heading for Kent.

'Time we gave this baby a bit of head,' said Jay, 'Turn Bruce up, or we won't be able to hear.' His foot squeezed the throttle. Bruce was drowned by the sound of an engine at a hundred and twenty miles an hour.

Heidi let go of the volume knob to clutch the edge of her seat with both hands. 'JAY, SLOW DOWN!'

He didn't hear her. Nor did he see in the driving mirror, as she did, the flashing of a blue patrol siren.

'JAY, IT'S THE POLICE!' He looked her way, trying to read her lips. 'THE COPS! THE PIGS – FUZZ – FILTH! BEHIND YOU!!'

'Oh shit!'

Jay slowed the car to ninety-five, but the police car was already level with them. It flashed past and disappeared out of sight.

'Bloody hell!' He was disappointed. 'After all that, they were chasing someone else! Who could be going faster than me, that's what I want to know!'

Disgruntled, he squeezed the throttle again.

'Jay, you're not Nikki bloody Lauda! I was terrified back there!'

'You – terrified? You're not scared of anything! Look at the way you push my brother around. How's that coming along, by the way?'

Heidi made a strangled snorting noise.

'Okay, okay, you don't want to talk about work. I'll buy that. But just for the record, you could do worse than to have a man like Ivo in your life.'

'I don't need one, thank you very much. I've already got a wonderful man in my life.' Heidi spoke without conviction.

A few miles further on, they found what the police had been looking for.

'Shit, look at that! A Ferrari Testarossa!'

They screeched to a halt on the hard shoulder. 'What a mean machine!' sighed Jay in tones of awe. 'A hundred-and-eight-grand's worth.'

'That makes it the most expensive piece of scrap metal in the world.' said Heidi sourly. The long, red wedge was concertina-ed into the length of a Mini. What had been the bonnet was now a charred, blackened lump.

'Christ, imagine owning a car like that!'

'Well, whoever owned it is presumably now dead.'

Jay's enthusiasm remained undented. 'God, that's the only way to go, though, isn't it? A hundred-and-forty and – blam! You know, I wish we could choose our own deaths. Because that's how I'd like to go – none of that cancer and old age crap. Into oblivion behind the wheel of my Twin-Cam turbo-charged Intercooler!'

Heidi got back into the said machine. 'For the moment, Jay, can we please just concentrate on staying alive?'

'Sure, sure, okay.' But he was still shaking his head in awe as he started the engine. 'A Testarossa! Now that's what I call a *cool* death!'

Byron Ferberger had big problems.

They were too big, too embarassing for him to take to the studios with him, so he retreated into his den at home. It was going to take a lot of phone calls to sort this one out, a hell of a lot.

The door burst open and Cherie marched in, five-inch heels teetering, lip gloss glistening. 'You bastard!' she shrieked. Byron did not look up from his notepad. This was a conventional opening gambit.

'How dare you? How dare you create a soap opera for that ugly little tramp when *I've* been asking you to get me into the movies for years!'

Byron folded his hands on the desk in front of him. 'Honey . . . honey . . . I know what it looks like, but believe me, it's not what it looks like.'

'Don't give me that bull, Byron!' Cherie's voice became suddenly gruff, but she checked it in time and returned to a shriek. 'I wanna part in this TV show and I want it now!' Her lilac locks quivered.

'Cherie, baby, I wouldn't *dream* of putting you through the embarrassment . . .'

Byron relaxed slightly, he was warming to it now, mastering the situation. Not for nothing did he have the reputation of being Hollywood's greatest wheeler-dealer.

' . . . Now I'm just trying to humour Melodie – jeez, *you* know what she's like! But we're talking low-budget stuff, and I mean *low*. Honey, you spend more on your grocery bill than I'm going to be spending on an episode. It's probably going to go out at seven o'clock on Sunday morning. I doubt we can even get it on the network. Now, you don't want your name to be associated with trash like that, do you?'

Cherie was starting to look very doubtful. It was working.

'What I have in mind for you is something much more glitzy. *Dynasty*, *Falcon Crest*, that kind of show. Lots of padded shoulders. Classy wigs. Or maybe even a mini series. Hell, we could even be talking major motion picture, if the right thing came up!'

Cherie left his office satisfied. Byron sighed with relief. Of course he had no intention of putting his wife in the movies. The dumb broad couldn't act her way out of a Vuitton bag.

But next to Melodie she was Meryl Streep. And with the camera adding at least ten pounds, they were going to have trouble fitting her into the frame. What a disaster this show was going to be! People weren't so dumb they'd believe his stupid, fat, lecherous daughter didn't get the part of the heroine because she was his daughter. His credibility would zero. He'd be the laughing stock of the West Coast. He'd have to cancel the whole thing before it was too late . . .

Then he remembered the polaroid photographs. Melodie had made damn sure he saw them. The most embarrassing thing about them was that his rug had come loose as his head bobbed up and down over Carla's sleek rear quarters. It looked as though something soft and furry was sitting on his face. And Melodie was threatening to sell them to the *National Inquirer*. He picked up the telephone and dialled.

'Hi, Nik, Byron here. How's it going?'

'Good. And you?'

'Good. Say, about that new project we talked about . . .'

'*Rambo* in period costume? Yeah, listen, we haven't got Sly Stallone to sign yet, but his agent says it's a definite maybe, so we're working on it. We've got a great title – *Gone to the Dogs* – whaddya think?'

'Great, great. But I want you to drop it.'

'Drop it? Shit Byron, this is the hottest – '

'I know, I know. Just for a little while, that's all I'm asking. Just long enough to knock me together, say . . . four thirty-minute episodes of a new soap.'

'Four episodes? No-one runs a series of only – '

'I know, I know, but with any luck the ratings will be

so bad the network'll cancel out. But I need a new show. I got me big trouble.'

'Well . . . I don't know Byron. I need time.'

'Do it Nik, you won't be sorry. I happen to know Steven Spielberg needs new writers. I could put in a word – '

'I'll do it, I'll do it. What kind of show you want?'

'I don't know . . . doctors/nurses, bosses/secretaries. Usual kind of daytime schlock. You don't even have to come up with any new storylines. We're talking crap here.'

'You got it!'

Byron hung up, relieved. But that had been the easy part. He dialled again.

'Glitzbitz Talent Agency, how-can-we-help-you?'

'Get me Terry Shapiro.'

A coy little tune played over the line while they put him through. 'Hi, Terry – Byron T. Fergerger here.'

'Byron! My man! Well, this is a pleasure!'

That was the thing about being a big shot, everyone was always pleased to hear from you. Until they heard what you had to say. 'Terry – I've got a new soap to cast and I need you to get me a lead. Male, Caucasian, twenty-five to thirty-five. The usual.'

'Hey, this is great news, Byron! I may even be able to get you Don Hassle.'

'Terrific. Call him.'

'So, who's he going to play opposite?'

Byron cleared his throat. 'Ur . . . my daughter.'

'You . . . you mean *Melodie*? . . . Listen, I don't know Byron. I think maybe Don has a booking. I'll just check . . . well, whaddya know, he has. Have you tried Randy Promo?'

It was the same story everywhere he tried. No-one could get him a male lead. They all suggested he tried Randy Promo, the biggest dead-beat among Hollywood's agents. Finally Byron did, but even Randy Promo, who was known to have found people to perform live acts with llamas, couldn't help. He wasn't surprised. No self-respecting actor would appear with Melodie Ferberger. It would be professional suicide.

It was a bad news day. Even Nik Warlock couldn't cheer him when he rang back to say he'd got a pilot episode together.

'The format's a shrink's clinic. I figured with analysis being so big, it would be an obvious scenario. The shrink falls in love with his patients, they fall for him, that kind of thing. Lots of sexual chemistry.'

'And Melodie?'

'She's the clinic nurse.'

Byron thought of Melodie in a nurse's uniform and groaned out loud.

'Wait till I hit you with this great title, though. *The Problem-Solver*.'

'That's shit. Sounds too much like *The Equalizer*.'

'How about just *Problems*. It's kind of intriguing.'

'Too tight-arsed. *Hang-ups* would be better. Yeah, let's call it *Hang-ups*!'

Leofred Plunkett stared up at the enormous gates to Byron Ferberger's Bel Air mansion. How did one get in? He couldn't see a doorbell, but there were several alarming television cameras pointed at his face. Eventually he located an electronic device with a notice saying 'SPEAK HERE'.

'Er . . . I'm Leofred Plunkett. I have an appointment with Mr Ferberger. I don't know . . . perhaps he's forgotten – '

'*Enter*' bleeped a computerised voice.

'Hi, I'm Cherie Ferberger,' said a beautiful woman on a lilac sofa. She was like an illustration from a health and beauty manual, but her voice was all wrong; high and squeaky, and when she spoke, the muscles in her face didn't move at all. 'And you are – ?'

'Leofred Plunkett.'

'Hi Fred! Byron will be with you in a second. Are you going to be in his new soap?'

'I don't think so.'

Byron came into the room, chomping a cigar and looking harassed. 'Hi Fred, how're you doing? Honey, this is the guy who smashed my Rolls. He's going to be working with Mom.'

'Aah.' The light of comprehension dawned on Cherie's face and she promptly started flicking through a magazine, all interest in Leofred lost.

'Come with me, Fred, there's someone I want you to meet.'

Mamie Ferberger, Byron's mother, lived in a separate wing of the house, so that no-one would have to bump into her. She suffered from a rare form of dementia which left her permanently believing that she was the Regency heroine of a Barbara Cartland novel.

'How does a hundred bucks a day sound Fred, for a coupla hours' work?'

'Fine, thank you.'

'Right, all you have to do is read to Mom here.' He pointed to a tiny old lady with blue-rinsed hair, who was surrounded by cheap reproduction Regency furniture and fake Gainsboroughs. She wore a long, high-waisted dress and elbow length gloves.

'You have to do a bit of acting, you know, get into the part. You read the hero's bits and she reads the heroine's. That's all you have to do. No physical contact.'

A delivery boy came in carrying a large cardboard box. 'Where shall I put this, ma'am?'

'Over there, my man!' trilled Mamie, in aristocratic tones.

'That'll be your costume,' explained Byron. 'Put it on.'

'Costume?'

'Yeah, you know, so you look like a Regency buck. That's what she wants.'

Inside the box were a pair of high-waisted pantaloons, a jacket and cravat and some tall, shiny boots. Boggling with disbelief, Leofred put on the jacket and cravat over his Mickey Mouse vest, salvaged from his night as a prostitute.

Byron handed him a copy of *Love's Broken Dream*. 'Okay, you're the Duke of Beaudesert. Read from here.'

'Er . . . "I love you, I love you, oh my little love, compared with you every woman I have known has been a disappointment!" '

'Is that why you have never married, your grace?' asked Mamie Ferberger.

'Not bad, not bad. You got the job.' Byron waved his cigar. 'Gotta go now. Carry on.'

Leofred cleared his throat and prepared to read on. Then he thought of the old lady and her poodle and experienced a sinking sense of *déjà vu*.

Charles Jolyon had made an important decision. He was going to leave his wife.

He sat upstairs in his study, rehearsing what he was going to say.

'*I feel that you and I have reached a point where we have nothing positive to offer one another . . .* '

Then he went downstairs for the conjugal confrontation.

Joy was on her hands and knees trying to retrieve wet clothes from the washing machine, which had broken down. A lake of soapy water seeped around her ankles.

Thaddeus and Clytemnestra were scooping up chunks of foam and throwing them at one another. The au pair was on the telephone, talking long distance . . .'

'Um, Joy – '

'Mind your feet, will you, I'm trying to clear up this mess!'

'It's about us, Joy. You see, I think we've reached a point, and I'm sure you must have felt this too, where – '

'Thaddeus! *Thaddeus! Don't* put that stuff in Clyte's hair . . . Charles, *do* something, will you!'

Charles waved his hands ineffectually over his children's heads, as if he was trying to cast a spell and turn them into agreeable, well-behaved children.

Joy watched him with withering contempt. Pulling a sopping T-shirt from the machine, she flapped it in their faces. '*Stop it at once, you horrible brats!*'

Temporary silence fell.

'Joy, we really have to talk. You see, I don't think things are working out very well between us – '

'So you're going to walk out? Is that it?' Joy delivered a pair of jeans from the womb of the washing machine with a loud SPLAT. '*And Helga, get off that bloody phone before I pull it out of the wall and wrap it around your neck! Next time you need to talk to Ulfric, send a telegram, it'll be cheaper!*'

The children found a jar of coffee beans and started scattering them on the waters. Charles wondered how long one got for dual infanticide.

'You're so predictable.' said Joy with satisfaction. 'You've got a bit bored, so you're going to move on. Ditch your children and your domestic responsibilities. Sit back while I struggle on here alone and you hang around in trendy wine bars and pick up secretaries at parties. Well it comes as no surprise, Charles. That's just about the

measure of most men. Now get out of my way, will you?'
She brandished a Squeegee at him.

'Joy, we *have* to talk about this! There are things going
on in my life that you know – '

'We *will* talk Charles. Later we will talk about your
complete lack of moral fibre. But right now, *I'm* going out.
Here – '

She handed him the mop, picked up the car keys and
swanned out, leaving Charles in the middle of a coffee-
stained floor, reflecting that leaving one's wife was a lot
harder than one might imagine.

Joy had far more important things on her mind than her
husband's conventional mid-life crisis. She didn't give him
a second thought as she leapt into the Volvo and roared
away. Outside the North London Women's Sorority, she
changed out of her cerise velour jogging suit and into a pair
of battledress trousers and a T-shirt that read 'PROPHY-
LACTIC MANUFACTURERS AGAINST THE POPE'.

The members of the sisterhood were eagerly awaiting
the arrival of their leader. They squatted on their pouffes,
dungarees ablaze with colour, CND badges flashing in the
light of the bare bulbs.

'Great news,' Tharka announced after she had called for
silence. 'We've been given the go-ahead for Phase One, so
now we can really see some action! This is going to be
bigger than Woodstock in '69! More controversial than
Greenham! Male domination is about to receive the ultimate
challenge!'

For the first time in his life, Ivo Cathcart was at a loss.

Having Heidi taken off his TV profile had driven him to
desperation. If only he could hit on something that she

really liked, something she enjoyed. Then he could weaken her with temptation.

She had sent back his cheque, neatly torn in two, with the message 'Just so you know I'm not going to cash it'. So she wasn't interested in money. What else was there? Power? He had bribed Jay into revealing her home telephone number and had started to phone her or, more frequently, her answering machine.

'Ivo Cathcart here. Would you be interested in becoming president of one of my subsidiaries?'

No response. Perhaps travel was more her line. 'Heidi, I have something you might like: a pair of tickets for the Orient Express . . .'

. . . 'A cruise in the Caribbean' . . . 'A trip to watch the test match in Australia' . . . 'a houseboat in Kashmir' . . . Travel, it seemed, was not one of Heidi Plunkett's priorities. Perhaps she wanted to meet famous people?

'Ivo Cathcart here . . . I've just been invited to a party by Michael Caine and his wife. Perhaps you'd like to join me? . . .'

This suggestion was met by expletives. He should have known that someone like Heidi would have a low opinion of celebrities.

He sought Jay's help again.

'Oh, yeah, I think she quite likes animals,' he said vaguely.

Ivo plunged in afresh. 'A season ticket to Regent's Park Zoo . . . your own racehorse . . . a stable of racehorses . . .' She almost weakened at the offer of a trip round Battersea Dogs' Home. And then Ivo phoned her answering machine and got a surprise. Instead of the usual message, which ran: *'To all my friends – I'm afraid I'm not here at the moment, so please leave your number, and to Ivo Cathcart – please piss off and leave me alone'*, he heard the following: *'Click, click – BEEP. Heidi here. I'm going to be away for a couple of weeks. I've gone to Los Angeles.'*

In that happy and temperate playground for the fortunate; Bel Air, California, Melodie Ferberger was busy for the first time in her life. Hairdressing frequency rose from three to five times a week, as did trips to the Lovely Nails Manicure Clinic. She even started going to exercise classes.

'Pre-production is just awesome,' she sighed on the phone to her friends. 'Everyone keeps wanting to take my picture.'

In fact one photographer had taken one thickly-vaselined shot for a publicity still.

Melodie started spending a lot of time on the phone. It was important that everyone should know what she was doing. 'My *own* show,' she told them, '*I'm* the star!'

'*Wow*, Melodie, that's terrific! Who's playing opposite you?'

'It's not decided yet,' said Melodie through her Snicklets Cola-flavoured gum.' That, at least, wasn't a lie.' Don Johnson wanted to do it, but he priced himself out of the market. They've thought about Tom Selleck . . .'

There was one phone call that was more important than all the others.

'Melodie Ferberger here,' . . . chew, chew . . . 'I wanna talk to Doctor Bodouski . . . I don't care if he has a client with him. Just tell him it's about the law-suit . . . Hiya, Doctor Bod, how're you doing? . . . I'm good too. Listen, I've got some great news for you. I've decided not to sue you for fucking up my nose and ruining my entire life if you'll do me another job . . . yeah, soon. I've gotta appear on TV . . . yeah, I wouldn't want to disappoint my fans either. So fix it up for me and I'll drop the charges. Byee.'

Melodie removed a little wet ball of gum and flipped it into the lilac tiled pool. On the newly laid Astroturf lawn, her grandmother reclined on a chaise longue while Leofred did an impressive rendering of the domineering, muscular-thighed Earl of Avebury.

'Hey, Daddy!' she shouted to her father as he passed by, weighted down by several cell phones and followed by an anxious secretary with a bottle of Hawaian Tropic. 'You know something, little ol' Fred's getting awful good at that macho stuff, and I think he's kinda cute, maybe – '

But her father wasn't listening. He had enough problems to solve, the problems of *Hang-ups*.

A few hours later, a jumbo jet from London circled in over the Ferbergers' swimming pool and headed south towards LAX.

Heidi Plunkett craned her neck and stared out of the window in wonder. Below her was a geometric carpet of fairy lights, spreading for sixty square miles. Infinite glitter that made London look like a small provincial town.

She was on a business trip, a big concession on the part of Mike Marshall. The condition attached was that when she returned, she was to go to work wherever she was placed, without argument. Heidi very much suspected that she would be put back on the Cathcart job. However, she would deal with that problem if, and when, it arose. For the moment there was her first trip to the States to consider.

TV Mayhem had arranged with its sister network, XYZ, that Heidi should spend some time with her opposite number, borrowing ideas from US shows and bringing them back across the Atlantic with her. The thought of American television programmes made Heidi shudder. She hoped she wouldn't feel that way about her hostess, in whose apartment she was going to be staying.

'Yoo-hoo!'

A large floral blob waved at her from across the barriers.

'*Hi!!*' She was greeted as though she were a long-lost relative. 'My *God*, it's so great to *see* you! I'm Miriam Grossley, XYZ. And you must be Heidi! Hi! I knew the minute I saw you. That poor girl, I thought. 'Has she missed out on the old UV rays, or *what*? And your hair, honey, your hair is to *die*. Never mind, we'll get that fixed. I'll take you to the beauty parlor, first thing. Okay, is that all you brought? Hope you brought a formal . . . okay, let's move . . . I want you to tell me all about yourself . . .'

Miriam was perfectly spherical, plump as a butterball. While most English women of that size would have tactfully beaten a retreat and not bothered with the details, Miriam had the sort of hair stylists would kill for; raven dark, falling in glossy waves. Her make-up must have taken at least an hour to perfect, co-ordinating exactly with the pastel shades in her flowered jogging suit. Her chubby fingers, bursting out of gorgeous dress rings, were tipped with long, gleaming fuchsia talons.

Miriam, Heidi discovered, talked all the time. She talked while she ate, while she drank, while she was in the shower, while other people talked. (She even confessed that her husband had divorced her on the grounds that she wouldn't stop talking while they were making love). She chattered her way through several red lights as they drove off in her VW Rabbit, and by the time they reached her home in Malibu, Heidi knew all about the fact that she had anorexia as a teenager, that her father suffered from impotence and that she'd had an abortion that she never told her ex-husband about.

' . . . a gynaecologist's a girl's best friend, that's what I always say. So . . . oh, you poor child, you must be *exhausted*. No problem though, we'll get you right under a comforter and you can crash out . . . Here we go, not much, but it's home and Larry Hagman's right around the corner . . .'

Miriam lived in a very pretty little house that seemed to be suspended off the edge of a cliff. Still, thought Heidi, as she peered through the picture windows, there was plenty of soft sand below them to break their fall.

'Like it?' asked Miriam anxiously. 'Only, I know you British live so differently to we do . . .'

Californian city dwellers appeared to like pretending that they lived in a cottage. There was a lot of basket-ware and patchwork and chintzy ruffles. Outside, in an odd contrast, the Pacific glittered invitingly. The beach seemed deserted.

'No-one swims here, they're too scared of the muggers and Chicano rapists,' confided Miriam. 'They all stay by their pools.'

She clucked around Heidi, tucking her into a put-you-up underneath a flowered duvet that she insisted Heidi needed, even though it was sweltering.

'Okay now, *tomorrow*, let's see; you'll come into work and see what goes on there, I'll take you to the beauty parlor . . . no, I insist, I'll treat you . . . lunch with the girls, and then there's a real important barbecue I want to take you to. I'll leave you to sleep now, I'm off to Post Aerobics.'

'Post aerobics?' In her jet-lag muddled state, Heidi imagined women weight-lifting with parcels and mail sacks.

'It's what people started to do when they realised that aerobics was bad for them,' Miriam explained. 'All that Jane Fonda go-for-the-burn garbage. Eugh, to die! . . .'

Heidi passed out. When she woke, Miriam was absent. She had no idea what time it was. The sun was shining, but here that could mean anything. On the door of the ice-box there was a note. '*Eat!*' it commanded. '*Watch TV. Back soon.*'

The ice-box was the size of a walk-in wardrobe. Heidi opened the door gingerly. Peanut butter in jars, peanut butter cookies, peanut butter flavour milk-shakes. Raw chicken livers, pounds of fillet steak. Five different types of mayonnaise. Six different flavours of ice-cream. 7–up, Coca-Cola, Dr Pepper's. Grape juice, mango juice, guava juice. Heidi closed the door again in despair. Where was she going to find something she could actually *eat*? She just fancied some Rice Krispies. And a cup of tea. On the work-top there were boxes of sachets with fancy tags; camomile, verbena, mint. But no actual *tea*.

Having settled for a can of beer and a piece of bread and jam, she switched on the TV. It took her a long time to work her way back to the first channel she had seen. There were at least twenty-five different ones. Well, not so different. Five of them were showing commercials for various peanut butter brands. And everyone looked a funny colour. Their hair was very yellow and their skin a pinky-orange. The older men had immaculately styled hair in a shade of pale blue.

Finally she found a weather forecast. One of the blue-haired men gave her an intimate smile. 'Hi!' he said, 'Things are going to be a little breezy tomorrow, with a little nip in the air and temperatures only reaching a chilly seventy-five degrees. So, time to light those log fires . . .'

Chilly? Seventy-five degrees? Heidi switched off in disgust. It was time she had a bit of sanity to cling to. She found the piece of paper with Leofred's number on it and punched it into Miriam's pink telephone.

'Ferberger residence,' said a foreign voice.

'Could I speak to Leofred Plunkett, please.'

'Larry *who*? Sorry, no-one of that name here.'

There was a click and the line went dead.

Disgruntled, Heidi flicked on the TV again. A commercial. Soft, romantic music. Two well-groomed smiling women with their arms around each other.

'*Hi, I'm Kathee. And this is my mother, Peggy . . .* '

Peggy smiled as she hugged her daughter. '*I use Mild-Moista douche, for all women who like to douche daily.*'

'*And I use Extra-Strength Moista,*' divulged Kathee, '*because I need greater cleansing power –* '

'Oh, for Christ's sake!' Heidi flung her head back and groaned. Welcome to Los Angeles.

Seven

'Wakey, wakey . . . time to go to the beauty parlor . . . here, here's coffee and a doughnut – enjoy, enjoy . . . you're welcome . . . My God you're so skinny! . . . look, don't mention it honey . . . GET OUTTA MY WAY, ASSHOLE! Jeez, these drivers, I have to pay four thousand bucks a year in insurance and that's just for the car, never mind my *life* . . . right, after you've had your hair fixed I'll take you to this great little boutique I know . . . not real expensive . . . designer labels . . . Calvin Klein . . . Norma Karmali . . .'

By the time Miriam had stopped talking, Heidi found herself beneath the hands of a hair stylist having honey-gold streaks woven into her hair. She was unable to remonstrate, trapped in the chair with each wrist gripped by a manicurist intent on painting her nails Sunset Peach. Miriam wasn't the sort of person you could have an argument with – she never let you speak for long enough for a start – so Heidi resigned herself to being transformed into an LA belle.

Having someone else in charge and not having to think made a pleasant change, and the hot sunshine was rapidly deadening her brain cells. When Miriam propelled her out of the Beverly Hills boutique, she was wearing a baby-pink linen jumpsuit and gold sandals.

'Just wait till they see you back home, you look *darling*.'

The first trip to Miriam's workplace was cursory in the extreme. XYZ's air-conditioned offices were on the studio lot of one of the major film companies, a place so vast that on arrival they were transported to the anonymous-looking building in something resembling a milk float on tracks.

Whilst Heidi's role developing new programmes placed her firmly at the bottom of TV Mayhem's ladder, Miriam seemed to be an incredibly important person at XYZ. She had a large, comfortable office, two secretaries and an enormous salary; and as far as Heidi could see, all she had to do was sit at her desk, glance at a few pieces of paper and telephone the odd executive producer. It was very peaceful. No-one rushed up and down corridors, shouting, as they did at TV Mayhem.

'Now – lunch with the girls!' announced Miriam.

'But Miriam,' remonstrated Heidi as the milk float took them back to the twenty-storey parking lot where the Rabbit was parked. 'I'm supposed to be here to work. They want me to look at your programmes and – '

'Later, later. First we have the lunch party. Well, it's kind of a women's group, actually. We get together, talk about our problems . . . DROP DEAD, ASSHOLE! . . . it's kind of therapeutic . . .'

Heidi remembered the North London Women's Sorority and wondered what she was in store for.

The weekly meeting of the A.M.A.A.P.A. (All Men Are A Pain In The Ass) was taking place beside the swimming pool of one of its members, the usual back-drop for such occasions. No need to hide in dimly lit basements when you have the Californian sunshine. Gorgeously dressed women in bright colours flitted about the pool like large, garish butterflies. The noise of their chatter almost drowned a far more important sound; the jangling of their jewellery. Those who were richest jangled loudest.

One such paragon was their hostess, Beattie Wate Lazen,

ex-wife of Dud Wate, Hollywood's king of spaghetti westerns, and Karl Lazen, XYZ's top chat show host. No need for another husband as she collected a dual fortune in alimony and spent it on entertaining 'the girls'. At one side of the pool was a huge trestle groaning with cold cuts and salads, smoked oysters and spinach mousse. The girls picked sparingly at the feast, protesting that they ate like birds, while they knocked back their iced margheritas and vodkatinis. Most of them were hungry, but they were as reluctant to confess their dependence on food as they were their dependence on men.

Everyone talked as much and as loudly as Miriam, exclaiming over one another's outfits and declaring themselves to be 'Good', 'Just terrific', 'The best'.

'My God, I just did Rodeo Drive in two hours, I'm all shopped out!' cried one woman, collapsing into a chair and requiring resuscitation with a highball. Here, it seemed, shopping was a recreation, a big game hunt. Heidi, who as infrequently as possible raced into a shop, bought what was necessary and raced out again, was nonplussed. She ate several cold chicken drumsticks and wiped her greasy fingers on the back of the pristine pink jumpsuit that Miriam had bought her.

Once honour had been satisfied, sun-block applied to lips and noses and more drinks poured by white-coated Mexican slaves, the session began. There was no squatting on bean-bags for the belles of Beverly Hills. Huge, squashy loungers were arranged in a circle by the slaves, and the women stretched themselves out Roman-style, slurping their cocktails and jangling their bracelets.

Heidi was the only newcomer, and had to be introduced at once. Sensing a complete lack of threat, the girls were enthusiastic in their welcome, even if they did talk as though Heidi wasn't really there. 'Oh Miriam,' they chorused, 'isn't she *darling*? Isn't she just the cutest?'

'Honey, you're going to tell us *all* about you,' insisted Beattie Wate Lazen, 'because we know everything about one another, isn't that right, girls?'

'Uh huh.'

'Sure is.'

' . . . But to make you feel more at home, honey, we'll tell you all about *us* first, okay?'

Heidi clenched her jaw muscles to stop herself from yawning. The strong, midday sun and the excesses of tequila were making her feel sleepy, and the lounger was so comfortable . . . With her face frozen in a grimace of a smile, she listened to an endless catalogue of broken marriages, divorce suits and months spent in analysis. Most of them had been married to at least one celebrity and all of them were anxious that Heidi – and preferably the whole of the British press too – should know that he was impotent/flatulent/ schizophrenic. Heidi wondered why, if they despised their ex-husbands so much, they were so keen to keep their names. They all had a cumulative string of surnames which they wore with pride, like so many scalps.

'Now, how about you, darlin'?' asked a pretty, plasticky blonde, who Heidi later discovered was Cherie Landers Scheistheim Powers Ferberger. 'Do you have a man in your life?'

'Two actually.' Heidi reluctantly admitted Ivo as 'the other man'. She had found, to her intense irritation that she quite missed his phone calls.

'*Tell us about them!*' came the unanimous cry.

Charles was first on the agenda.

'No way!'

'Uh *uh!*'

'Keep away honey!'

To Heidi's surprise, the girls all seemed put off by the fact that he was married. Since marriage was such a disposable commodity in Los Angeles, she had expected this problem to be dismissed as a mere detail.

It was, however, of secondary importance. Ivo provoked a similar reaction, until Heidi confessed that he owned just about everything in Britain. There were screeches of delight amid the chiming of Cartier.

'Go for it!'

'What are you waiting for? Jesus, *I* should be so lucky! Who gets John Paul Getty knocking on their door and turns him down?'

Heidi made an earnest attempt at explaining Charles' importance, though on the sun-drenched shores of Beattie's swimming pool she had to admit that it sounded rather feeble. 'He makes me feel wonderful . . .'

'Never mind that, honey, how does your bank account feel?'

They thought that Ivo sounded great, and simply couldn't understand why she didn't want him. The fact that he looked like a pig carried no weight at all.

'So? You get a good plastic surgeon,' said a woman who numbered Ferberger among her list of surnames. There were several of Byron's ex-wives present.

Dismissing Heidi's case as hopeless, they focused their attention on the reasons for her visit to LA. And as it turned out, they were far less interested in her mission for TV Mayhem than in the fact that she hoped to meet up with her brother.

' . . . And he's only twenty? Say, isn't that the greatest? What does he do, honey?'

There was a sudden spark of animation from Cherie Ferberger. 'Don't tell me – you're Fred Plunkett's sister! My God, he's my husband's latest discovery. Darlin' your brother is a *star*!'

*

Exhausted and hungover after the lunchtime symposium, Heidi had to psych herself up for a barbecue at six. This involved showering, being liberally smeared with lip gloss and climbing into a suitable outfit, borrowed from Miriam. Heidi couldn't understand how Miriam came to have so many clothes that were several sizes too small, until it dawned on her that she had morbid fantasies about being thin.

'I thought this was so cute,' she'd say, 'And of course they only had it in a size 12, but I thought to myself, "What the hell, you can starve yourself into it . . . "'

' . . . You're going to have a real good time tonight, I just know it,' said Miriam as the Rabbit sped along Ventura. 'You're going to meet all sorts of real neat people. All the guys play polo – we are talking rich, rich, *rich* . . .'

Their destination was Pacific Palisades, a suburb between Santa Monica and Malibu that featured chic little shopping malls and Spanish style ranch houses built into the cliffs. The party was at one such house. Everyone was beautiful, everyone had a sun-tan. Almost everyone was dressed in white. Almost everyone was in The Industry.

'Hi, I'm Dean.' A stunningly handsome man appeared at Heidi's elbow and seemed to find her the most fascinating woman since Garbo. For five minutes. But it was only because he thought Heidi might be an important producer or director (Dean was an out-of-work actor) and as soon as he found out that she was a nobody from England he drifted away.

Whether they were actors, writers or producers, Heidi's fellow guests all shared the same anxiety. They were desperate to be seen to be doing something important. They would have been happier to walk down Sunset Boulevard naked than to admit to doing nothing. There was a lot of talk about projects in development, pre-development or even 'in conception'.

After several hours of failing to find out how anyone actually *earned* the money to pay for their Giorgio Armani and Azzedine Alaia, Heidi had had enough. She escaped onto the balcony, where stars glittered in an inky sky and the Pacific was sighing against the rocks below. Closing her eyes, she let the sea breeze cool her cheeks. Inside, someone was passing round a joint; she caught whiffs of the sickly sweet smell wafting through the open doors.

'Heidi!'

She stared. No-one here knew her name, let alone anyone English.

'Heidi, it's me.'

'Leof! Good God, I didn't recognise you!'

'I didn't recognise you at first, either. Your hair's gone a funny colour.'

'It's called "Honey Gold". I've been California-ised. So have you, from the look of you . . . what have they done? . . . I can't quite place it . . .'

'It's my teeth,' said Leofred sadly, 'They said they weren't good enough for television.'

'You mean – '

'Fifteen hours at the dentist. They capped every single one of them.'

'Dear God!' Heidi continued to stare at her brother. He'd always had a very neat appearance. He still looked neat, but he also looked smooth. The sea breeze failed to ruffle his newly side-parted hair, thanks to a generous layer of hairspray. His sports slacks had a crease you could have cut cheese with.

'Are you *really* going on television?' she demanded. She grabbed a piece of key lime pie from the plate he was holding and bit into it, smearing her pastel lip gloss onto her chin. 'Someone told me you were going to appear in a soap opera, but I said they must have got the wrong person. After all, you can't act.'

'Apparently that doesn't matter,' said Leofred. He seemed resigned. Being talent-spotted by a movie producer was something that had just *happened*, like everything else in his life.

'Well, at least you're going to make a fortune.'

'Not necessarily.' Leofred fiddled with the collar of his Brooks Brothers shirt. 'It's, er . . . very low budget and they're only making a few episodes. We start filming tomorrow.'

Heidi was wondering if it would be worth saying goodbye to Charles forever, packing in her job at TV Mayhem and waiting until someone spotted her. 'Shooting,' she corrected in a bossy elder sister's tone, 'and surely what happens is all quite straightforward? Go along there tomorrow and do all you can to make it a success and then maybe it'll run longer.'

Leofred shook his head. 'It's not straightforward at all. You see, Ferberger doesn't *want* me to try. In fact he's offered me a cash bonus if I help make *Hang-ups* a complete failure.'

'Okay everybody, let's have some quiet on the set please. We're about to go for the first take . . .'

Leofred was sitting on a canvas chair marked 'FRED PLUNKETT', staring at his copy of the script in disbelief.

'*Dr Caspar is a mature, fortyish guy. He's seen the world, been around. Ten years ago, he survived the rigors of a broken marriage.*'

Surely no audience was going to swallow *this*? A twenty-year-old student playing a forty-year-old psychiatrist? But Byron Ferberger had insisted. He had insisted that no other actor could play the part. So the Make-Up department had etched a few wrinkles around his eyes and painted streaks of what looked like grey Tippex onto the hair around his temples. Naturally this only served to accentuate his immaturity, especially when he opened his mouth. His voice was high and squeaky with nerves. He couldn't even do a decent American accent, but Ferberger had told him not to change the way he spoke. Instead he had persuaded the script-writing team to work in the fact that Caspar had been educated at Oxford.

'Okay, let's have the principals on their marks please, for a lighting check.'

That meant Leofred and Melodie Ferberger, who was to play Caspar's nurse/receptionist, Tempest Jensen.

'Oh Christ,' muttered the director, 'I thought we told her to kill the braces!'

Melodie, with two inch fingernails and a resplendent platinum mane from the wig department, had levered her ample form into a skimpy white overall that stopped a few inches below her crotch. Her plump feet spilled over the sides of white stilettos.

'Melodie, Melodie sweetheart, listen – '

'Do what?' The kilogram of chrome on Melodie's teeth flashed as the lighting men moved the studio lamps in closer.

'Melodie, don't chew gum dear, we're going for a take. And I thought the stylists had agreed, no braces.'

'My dentist said he couldn't allow me to take part if I was going to discontinue my treatment.'

'*Couldn't allow you? . . . Jesus Christ!* . . . okay, okay, just don't open your lips too far when you talk. And I hope you know your lines because we're ready to shoot . . . Fred, on your mark please . . . and . . . ACTION!'

The first shot was a little establishing scene between the two main characters, building up a picture of their relationship. Leofred had been horrified to discover that '*Tempest is concealing a deep passion for her boss*' and '*Caspar is struggling to repress a powerful attraction to his beautiful assistant, an attraction that threatens his professionalism . . .'*

The first scene – as did all the scenes for the sake of economy – took place in Caspar's consulting room. A plywood set had been built, complete with carpet, sober striped wallpaper, a shelf of cardboard book façades and a hatstand that was nailed to the floor in the cause of continuity. The desk that Leofred was to sit behind had pens and paper weights that you couldn't lift up, plus the obligatory pile of blank 'papers'.

He leaned his elbows on the desk, fiddled with a glued-down pen and tried to look forty. Melodie perched on the edge of the desk, revealing acres of thigh and moistening her lips lustfully.

'And . . . ACTION!'

'Gee, Doctor Caspar, it's real inneresting when you talk to me about your days at the University of Oxford, England. LOOKS AT HIM WITH DEVOTION. REVERSE ANGLE TO CASPAR – '

'*Cut!* Melodie . . . sweetie . . . the bits in capitals are the directions. You don't have to say those bits.'

'You serious? I thought you said to learn everything!' Melodie pouted.

'No, only the things that Tempest has to *say*. Okay, let's go again, from the top, take two and . . . ACTION!'

'Gee, Doctor Caspar, it's real inneresting when you talk to me about your days at the University of Oxford, England. Looks at him with devotion.'

The director was sweating visibly. 'Melodie, just stop after "England". And less teeth, *please*.'

The first scene needed twenty-three takes, and then it was time for lunch. The director was threatening to quit and only a hefty bribe from Ferberger secured his return to the set. Munching his hero sandwich, Leofred reflected gloomily that at least starring with Melodie was making him look like Richard Burton. He flicked through the pages of the afternoon's shooting script and saw that Tempest was due to reveal her true feelings to Doctor Caspar.

'Oh Doctor . . .' lisped Melodie, the seams of her white uniform straining, 'The reason I have never married is because here, deep in my heart . . .' She clutched at her heaving bosom, ' . . . I have only ever cared for you.'

Through her parted lips, Leofred could see a wad of purple gum. He was so transfixed by its gentle rocking movements, to and fro between her molars, that he almost forgot his next line.

'Er . . . Tempest, you know our relationship can never be more – '

The brilliant studio lights were suddenly obscured as Melodie's body loomed across his field of vision and then towards his face as she crossed the desk with surprising agility. Leofred was just extricating his nose from her cleavage when she swooped on his mouth, weaving her tongue between his lips and impaling his lips on her metal brace. The purple gum lodged itself in his throat and he began to choke. Waving his arms and legs wildly he pulled away from the desk, dragging Melodie with him. The two of them toppled onto the immoveable hatstand, which snapped at the base and crashed to the floor like a falling tree.

'*Cut!* Melodie, what the fuck are you doing? There's nothing in the script about getting into a clinch!!'

Melodie extricated herself, looking around for her missing gum. 'Well, like, I was really getting into the character of Tempest, so I thought I should improvise a little.'

'Melodie, I don't want you to improvise! Do anything, but not that? Have you got it?'

Muttering to himself about Leofred's life insurance company having good cause to sue, the director went to call his lawyer. The only hope for his career now was if the television company staged a total network shutdown.

'Jesus! Will you look at this schlock?'

Miriam and Heidi were watching the shooting of *Hangups* at the Real Life studios, where many of XYZ's television shows were taped.

'Can you believe XYZ are actually *buying* this stuff?' demanded Miriam as Melodie scrambled about on Caspar's desk, stuffing her breasts back into her dress, 'It's so bad it's unreal! I sure hope your brother knows what he's doing.'

Heidi, who had rather enjoyed the scene, tried to catch Leofred's eye, but he was sitting with his head buried in his hands.

'Okay, now . . . what can we show you?' Miriam took hold of Heidi's elbow and led her across the floor of the vast studio lot. 'We have several great new shows shooting here right now . . . this one right here is *Doggy Dating*. Do you have this in England? . . . No? . . . Honey, you're gonna *love* this one . . .'

Sitting on a row of stools were three dogs, of various shapes and sizes, with their respective owners standing behind them, murmuring words of encouragement. On the other side of a moveable screen was a fourth dog, a poodle.

'Now everybody, I'd like you to meet Muffin,' said a statuesque blonde hostess with tombstone teeth and a plunging chiffon housecoat, 'Everybody say "Hi, Muffin!" Muffin's here to choose herself a date, and it's going to be one of our three lucky contestants behind the screen . . . Right, Muffin, would you like to ask your first question?'

Muffin stared at the ceiling, uninterested while her owner read from a card. 'Dog Number One: if we were on our first walk together, would you take me for a romp through a pile of dried leaves or to an interesting little lamp-post you know, and why?'

Dog Number One, a slavering boxer, sniffed the seat of his stool. His owner chewed her lip for a while and then said, with complete sincerity, 'Gee, I think I'd do both! How about a brisk trot through the woods, followed by a cruise round our favourite lamp-posts?'

'Sounds good to me!' said Muffin's owner. 'Okay, Dog Number Two . . .'

'What do you think?' Miriam demanded of Heidi.

'Well – '

'Hey look, we've got something great over here, this is one of my favourites . . .' Miriam dragged Heidi to another corner of the lot where an audience were seated beneath a blaze of lights. ' . . . *Celebrity Undies*.'

A young man with the obligatory fluorescent teeth was standing beneath a flashing pink neon sign in the shape of a pair of underpants. He grinned, waiting for the applause to die down. 'Good evening ladies and gentlemen . . . tonight on *Celebrity Undies* we'll be finding out who has been sleeping in this . . .' A picture of a flimsy silk negligee flashed up on a huge screen behind him. ' . . . And who is the owner of *this* collection of boxer shorts? I'll give you a clue – it's not Bruce Willis! . . .'

Miriam's rapt attention was distracted by a fanfare behind them. 'Oh my *God*! Look at this, Heidi, you must look at this! It's *All or Nothing*, the most popular game in the States at the moment! C'mon . . .'

Yet another host, dressed in a suit made from a lurex star-spangled banner, was explaining the rules of the game to a screaming, hysterical audience. Above his head was a canopy stuffed with red, white and blue balloons. It bulged ominously.

'Now, remember folks, the rules are easy! When I spin

the wheel, the needle can end on a white, a red, or a blue square. If it's white, I spin again. If it's blue, you win a million dollars . . . but if it's *red* . . . that means you have to give everything away – your house, your car, your life insurance policy – it all goes to a charity of your choice. Now, will tonight's lucky contestant please come on down! . . .'

A roving spotlight picked out a girl wearing a badge that said 'LOU-ANNE'.

'Come on down, Lou-Anne!'

Lou-Anne stumbled, sobbing, onto the stage. 'She doesn't look very happy,' observed Heidi from her position on the edge of the set.

'Are you kidding? Those are tears of joy! People would sell their grandmothers to get on this show . . .'

The wheel was spun, and landed on red. The shrieks from the audience reached fever pitch and the ill-fated Lou-Anne fainted into the arms of the host.

'Time to go,' Miriam mouthed over the din. 'We'd better leave for the airport if you're going to catch that flight home.'

She led Heidi away as Lou-Anne was swamped in balloons and a chorus of 'God Bless America'. 'Remember folks,' the host was saying, 'it's not the winning that counts, it's the taking part . . .'

Miriam gave a deep sigh. 'Honey, I sure am going to miss having you around to talk to . . .'

Heidi opened her mouth to reply in a similar vein, but was cut off by the unceasing flow. ' . . . So, when you get back to England, you're going to have to decide, honey.'

'Well, I quite liked the one with the underwear . . .' began Heidi, 'but – '

'No, not about the shows, dummy, about the two men! Which one is it going to be? The good-looking creep or the rich ugly one?'

Eight

On her first day back at the headquarters of TV Mayhem, Heidi gave a debriefing on her trip to Los Angeles.

' . . . so, we could risk getting arrested for poking around in people's knicker drawers, or get people to donate their houses to charity and have the campaigners for the homeless on our backs.'

With this defiant conclusion, Heidi flung down her pen and stared defiantly at her audience of Mike Marshall, Charles Jolyon and Charles' secretary, Megan.

Mike scratched his ear with his biro and looked thoughtful. 'Yah . . . liked the thing with the dogs, though. Perhaps if we could get Cilla Black to front it . . . good work, Heidi. You can tell XYZ we'll be in touch.'

Charles said nothing until Mike and Megan had left, then he pounced, crushing Heidi against the filing cabinet.

'Oh darling, I've missed you so much, it's so great to see you . . .'

He fondled her buttocks protectively, and in Pavlovian response Heidi felt her hands go up to the back of his neck and entwine themselves in his luxuriant curls. She had been longing to see him . . . But something felt different.

She cleared her throat. 'Charles . . . while I was away, I did some thinking.'

'Mmmmmn . . .' He busied himself with nuzzling her throat.

'And I decided I can't go on seeing you. Unless you agree to leave your wife.'

Charles dropped her abruptly. 'Heidi, be responsible, it's not as simple as all that . . . many factors to consider . . . family responsibilities . . .'

'Leave her,' said Heidi baldly. She swept a well-chewed biro, a half-eaten Mars bar and a used Kleenex into her briefcase. 'Otherwise, forget it.'

Delivering an ultimatum to Charles left her feeling jubilant. She positively swaggered up the steps of Rapier Industries and into Ivo Cathcart's office.

Ivo, however, seemed subdued. He didn't comment either on her sun-tan or on her newly-streaked hair, as she had expected him to. For once he seemed intent on the business in hand.

Heidi fidgeted in her chair. 'So,' she said, bent on provocation, 'what are you going to offer me this time? An island in the Indian ocean? *Two* million pounds?'

'Nothing.' Ivo didn't look up from the company report he was reading.

'What?'

'I said I wasn't going to offer you anything. Any businessman knows that you only waste time pursuing a non-visible proposition, and time is money. In my case, a thousand pounds a minute. Besides, sex is a buyer's market. I can look elsewhere.'

'Oh.'

'So, shall we get on with the interview?'

He started to tell the tape-recorder about his recent acquisition of a cable network in Italy. Heidi picked at her fingernails and let her eyes flick about the room. There was evidence of success everywhere she looked. The Queen's Award for Industry stood next to the Businessman of the

Year Trophy. There was a framed photograph of Ivo receiving the red book from Eamonn Andrews on *This is Your Life*, another of his squat and pig-like figure next to Terry Wogan. She sighed. The thing about successful men was that you could not make them do something they didn't want to do. It was useless playing games with Pig-Face.

' . . . I think that's about all you need for the moment.'

Heidi switched off the tape-recorder and scooped it into her briefcase. 'Right. Only one more session to do then, on your home life. Have someone ring and fix a time.'

She had already scuffed her way to the door when Ivo stopped her. 'Wait a minute Heidi, I've just thought of something. My wife's having a dinner party tonight; the perfect material on my home life. I want you to come along.'

'I can't.'

'Why not?'

'It's too far. I haven't got a car, and it'll be too late to take a train back.'

'My driver can take you. Or better still . . .' He smiled faintly, ' . . . Stay the night.'

Linda Cathcart was giving an exclusive interview.

Draped elegantly over a Designer's Guild sofa, she told an over-awed junior reporter lots of lies about her life-style while a photographer scurried about with a silver umbrella getting pictures for the glossy six-page spread in *Rich Living* magazine.

'So Mrs Cathcart, let me just check that I've got this right . . .' The reporter went over the notes on her pad, 'You run your own design consultancy and raise three children whilst maintaining a beautiful Hampshire home and giving your famous husband all the support he needs in his business enterprises – is that right?'

'Exactly right.' purred Linda, tossing her long glossy blonde hair over her left shoulder-pad. 'Now, you absolutely *must* get some pictures of me with the children. Excuse me a minute – '

She unclipped her Chanel baroque earring so that she could put the receiver of the internal telephone to her ear. 'Susie, I want the children down here for a picture . . . that's too bad, you'll just have to wake him! And I want them in their best!'

Realising that she had been overheard snapping like a she-terrier, Linda turned a beaming smile on the confused reporter. There were a few tense moments, until the brown-uniformed nanny brought in three young children in improbably white clothes. Linda cradled the baby for the photograph.

'How old is . . . er, it?' enquired the reporter.

'Six weeks.'

'Seven.' corrected the nanny.

But Linda Cathcart had the situation far too well under control to worry about minor details. 'Now I'm going to go and change into another outfit, and I want you to do some shots in the dining room.'

She re-appeared twenty minutes later, better groomed and more stylish than ever before.

'Like this, I think . . .' She tweaked at an arrangement of orange tiger lilies on the huge dining table, which was being laid for twenty-four. The photographer snapped away obediently. ' . . . And the caption I want you to use is: *Mrs Ivo Cathcart, in an orange silk Jasper Conran, personally attends to her husband's business entertaining.*' . . .

Five hours later, the caterers had finished their work on

the table and twenty-two guests were slurping noisily at their lobster bisque. Ivo and Linda Cathcart graced each end of the table, looking the perfect host and hostess in the warm glow of the candles. With a rush of irritation Linda realised that she should have made the photographer from *Rich Living* stay and record this happy scene.

Heidi, lost somewhere in the middle ranks of the table, had never felt more out of place in all her life. It was even worse than being adrift in a ranch-house in Pacific Palisades. Here there was nowhere to hide, and since she had committed herself to staying the night, she couldn't even leave.

On her left was the chairman of the advertising agency Spink Oddman Brown, who kept putting his right hand on her thigh and then pretending that he'd really meant to put it in his lap.

'This year we're going on a package holiday,' he told Heidi. 'You know, you get the whole island, the villa and the deep-sea fishing boat in one package. Only fifty grand a week.' He put his hand back on her left thigh. 'Sorry, just looking for m'napkin.'

The woman opposite wore the biggest jewels that Heidi had ever seen. She now wished she hadn't bothered with the chainstore fake diamanté that she'd bought to smarten up her black T-shirt and scruffy black skirt.

'That necklace is very pretty,' sighed the woman, 'and no-one would ever guess that the real thing was in the bank vaults, if it weren't for the boring old problem of insurance.'

So these people couldn't tell the difference, having first made the assumption that she was as rich as they were. Her two pounds ninety-five had been well spent after all.

'The marvellous thing about our new place,' said the jewel woman, whose husband had just bought a penthouse in Chelsea Wharf, 'is being so close to P.J.' P.J. – Heidi had deduced, was Peter Jones. 'They do the most marvellous shoe trees.'

'Really?' Heidi's jaw ached with the effort of not laughing or, eventually, of not screaming. The dining room was unbearably hot and stuffy because a fire had been lit in the marble fireplace even though it was August, just to show off. She wanted to strip off her sweat-dampened T-shirt and run bare-breasted up and down the table, plunging her espadrilles into the asparagus mousse. She fantasised for a moment about doing just that. There wasn't much else to do. Every time she looked in Ivo's direction, he pretended he hadn't noticed. Every time she looked the other way, Linda, supple as a tiger in her gold lamé Bruce Oldfield, pierced her with an look of ill-disguised contempt.

Finally she stood up, her skirt clinging in a creased lump to her backside and the backs of her legs. 'If you'll excuse me, I think I'll retire now. I don't feel . . . very well.'

'Nothing to do with the food, I hope?' asked Linda, poison thinly veiled behind the dazzling smile.

Ivo stood up too. 'I'll show you to your room.' He led her out of the house and down a moonlit path. She had to trot to keep pace with his energetic stride.

'Christ, I'm glad to get outside!' she said.

Ivo slowed down. The braying of laughter and the rattle of coffee cups were still audible somewhere in the distance. '*You're* glad! I thought I'd go crazy if I stayed in that room a minute longer.'

'I thought those people were your friends.'

He gave a pig-like snort. 'I can't stand most of them! They're Linda's friends. I do this once in a while to humour her, then we go our separate ways again.'

'She was looking daggers at me.'

'Of course.' He smiled. 'She thinks we're having an affair.'

'Oh.'

They continued along the path, almost a quarter of a mile from the house now. 'Where am I staying, the dog kennels?'

'The guest chalet.'

It was something like the house that Snow White shared with the dwarves, only instead of seven small beds there was one vast one covered with lace pillows. There was even a miniature en suite bathroom with bidet.

'Right, have you got your luggage?'

Heidi pointed to a small red sausage bag made from waterproof nylon, its stained and grubby sides held together with a safety pin.

'Is that all you've got?' Ivo stared at the scruffy object with a sort of longing. 'What's inside it?'

'You know – just night things and a change of under-wear.' Heidi was suspicious. 'Why, what's it got to do with you?'

'D'you mind if I stay and watch you unpack?'

'Suppose not,' said Heidi ungraciously. She unpinned the bag and took out her balding bathrobe, a Winnie the Pooh T-shirt and a grotty sponge bag that she'd had since she went to Girl Guide camp at the age of ten. They looked very odd, lying there on Linda Cathcart's satin bedspread.

She expected Ivo to make a pass at her as a matter of course, but he didn't. He did just what he had said he was going to do – he watched her, gazing hungrily at her belongings. Then he wished her goodnight and left her.

Ivo clenched his fists as he walked up the path, away from the chalet. In bed, Heidi pulled the sheets tight around her shoulders. Both of them were in the grip of fantasy.

On the set of *Hang-ups*, things were going from bad to worse.

Leofred arrived at the studio for the shooting of the final episode and was quite unable to locate the mock-up of Doctor Caspar's office, with its familiar striped wallpaper and battened-down hat-stand. It had completely disappeared. He went outside again and checked, but yes, he was in the right place. Lot 15. The crew were as confused as he was.

The director burst into the building, waving a piece of paper. He was at least a stone lighter than he had been at the start of the series, and his face had a haggard look.

'I *don't* believe it!' he screamed, 'I do *not* fucking believe it! Look at this, will you!'

They gathered around him in a little huddle while he read the contents of the letter.

'Hiya everybody! Hope you like it! The set, I mean! I thought Doctor Caspar's little old office was looking totally dull, so I had it fixed. The interior decorators I used are just awesome. Anyways, I'm afraid I've got to call in sick for a few days, but I'll be back with you all just as soon as I can. Love and kisses, Melodie xxx'

'Oh Jesus,' the director groaned, like a dying man. 'This is just the end. Can you believe this?'

In silence, they contemplated what had once been Doctor Caspar's consulting room, now a froth of lie-lack frills and flounces, with cute little cushions and flower arrangements everywhere.

'We'll have to write it into the script,' sighed the director, 'We're only scheduled for one more day's shooting, there's no time to change it. We've got to get that bird-brain back on the set now, to finish off this pile of shit. There's a hundred buck bonus for the guy who tracks down the stupid bitch! Call Ferberger!'

There was a rush to the telephones. Byron Ferberger was recuperating at a health farm in Mexico. Cherie Ferberger said she didn't know where her step-daughter was, she only knew that her appointments diary had the entry 'Doctor Bodouski'.

Melodie was finally tracked down in a Bel Air clinic, recovering from another disastrous nose-job. It was Leofred who was deputed to go and lure her back to work, on the grounds that since she had the hots for him he would be the one with the most bargaining power.

He found her in bed, surrounded by baskets of flowers that she had sent herself. Her head was heavily bandaged with only her eyes visible.

'Ohnnn Fnnn . . .' she wailed through the bandages that covered her mouth.

Leofred was about to ask whether it had been strictly necessary for the nurses to prevent her from talking, then realised this was a foolish question. 'Here, let me help you,' he offered, peeling back a layer so that she could move her lips.

'Fred, honey,' cooed Melodie, trying to bat her eyelashes beneath the bandages, 'Did I ever tell you you're a real babe. To the max.'

'Ah, . . .' Leofred felt himself blushing. 'The thing is, they want you back at work straightaway. They said not to worry about the . . . er . . . nose. They said Make-Up can cover the bruises, and they can use long shots.'

'Oh Fred, I *can't*!' Melodie started wailing again. 'Don't you see, this is the biggest disaster in the history of the universe – period.'

'What happened exactly?'

'I asked for "Tiptilted" but he got the diagrams upside down and I ended up with "Ski-Jump". I can't possibly be seen in public until he's had time to correct it. I can't disappoint my fans. You understand that, don't you Fred?'

The only thing Leofred understood was that no-one could be a worse actress than Melodie. 'But you're in breach of contract. They'll sue you.'

'So?' Melodie inserted a Chiclet through the opening that Leofred had made and chewed away as energetically as the bandaging would allow. 'So? They sue me, I sue Doctor Bod. Anyhow, you're forgetting that Byron Ferberger is my daddy. He'd never sue me.'

Byron Ferberger, at that moment flying from Acapulco to a *Hang-ups* crisis meeting, would have liked nothing more than to sue his daughter. But unfortunately there were too many stories she could sell to the press.

The only possible compromise was a stand-in. And since there wasn't a single actress in Hollywood who would have risked herself in the part of Tempest Jensen, the solution didn't take long to find. The studio was booked for an extra late night session, and Leofred was taken personally by Ferberger to meet his new co-star.

'Here she is, Fred!'

'Sorry . . . where?' Leofred couldn't see anybody.

'The dummy, dummy.'

Byron pointed at the chair by the side of the desk. A large blow-up doll in a nurse's uniform and a blonde wig was perched on it, her legs thrown apart at a rakish angle.

'But surely . . .'

Leofred was so aghast, he was stammering. He conjured up visions of British Broadcasting Standards, the Trade Descriptions Act and the obscenity laws. 'Surely the audiences won't . . . er . . . accept it?'

'Sure, why not?' Byron patted Leofred on the back with a suntan-oiled paw. 'Look at it this way, she's gotta be a better actress than my daughter.'

Leofred couldn't argue with that.

' . . . And we'll haveta cut out all the close-ups. They'll never know.'

Feeling certain they would, Leofred said desperately, 'But we're about to shoot a big love scene, aren't we? I mean – '

'Forget it, Fred. We'll just write out Melodie's lines. You'll get to do all the talking, and we'll pad the whole thing out with a bit of heavy action, know what I mean!'

Leofred did, and he was dreading it. It was bad enough having to pace up and down in full make-up, with his distinguished greying temples painted in, talking to a blow-up doll.

'Tempest, Tempest, do you know how you drive me crazy?' he demanded. He fixed the plastic face with what he hoped was a demonic stare as the camera moved in for a close-up. 'To me, you are like no other woman . . .'

'Great, great!' enthused Byron from the sidelines. 'Now let's move in for some action!'

The directions read; *Caspar scoops Tempest into his arms and embraces her fiercely as though he will never let go . . .*

'He will never let go' is just about the size of it, thought Leofred, whose thighs were wedged onto the chair where the doll was arranged in an abandoned pose. For as he leaned over to embrace her, the top of his fly zipper caught on the hem of her white dress.

'Come on now!' shouted the director, 'Let's see that action, we're going for a take.'

Leofred tried to signal his need for help, but the cameras were already rolling. '*I can't . . . I can't!*'

Byron pushed past the director, his huge oiled body gleaming under the lamps. 'You can't get it up? Jesus, whaddya want, realism? You don't haveta get it up, just kiss her!'

'*I can't move!*' Leofred struggled to extract himself, but the teeth of his zip stuck into Tempest's plastic thigh. There was a loud explosion as the doll burst.

'CUT!'

At seven o'clock on the morning after the show went out,

Leofred was summoned personally to Ferberger's mansion. He didn't understand why. He could hardly be fired now, after he had filmed four episodes and fulfilled his contract. He was even eligible for the 'turkey' cash bonus.

'It's all right, Mr Ferberger,' he said, facing him across the gargantuan desk in the den, 'I was going to leave town anyway. I thought I'd use my earnings to travel a bit . . . go up to San Francisco, maybe to Carmel – '

'You sure won't!' boomed Byron. 'You will go nowhere, not now!' He tossed the morning edition of the *LA Times* across the desk.

'*XYZ SCORES WITH HANG-UPS*' read the headline, '*Comedy show hits top of ratings.*'

There was a fuzzy still of Leofred and the doll.

'You're signing a new contract kid, we've got a hit on our hands.' He pointed a cigar at the photo. 'And I got me a new star.'

Leofred blinked with disbelief.

'Not you, the dummy!'

The hard, funky rock music upped its tempo. Jay Cathcart, star of the Levis commercial, swung into action. He slithered around the room, undulating his hips in time to the beat. His hair, still wet from the shower, was slicked back close to his skull; his naked, suntanned torso rose gracefully from the waist-band of the rugged denim jeans. With feline agility he leapt into the sofa, twisted on one foot and hit the floor again, straight into a fast jive . . .

The buzzing of the entryphone interrupted Jay's fantasy. Switching the stereo down to a bearable level, he picked up the handset.

'*God, you're a bloody pain, Jay! I've been ringing this thing for ten minutes!*' Ivo's voice crackled over the intercom.

' . . . Just as well I didn't waste my time calling at your office' he observed drily once Jay had admitted him, glancing at his watch. It was only five-thirty. 'Had a strenuous day, have we?'

'Well, yeah, sort of.' Jay busied himself with towelling his wet hair. 'Want a drink?' He tossed his brother a bottle of Schlitz.

'I've decided . . .' said Ivo slowly, flicking off the bottle top with one precise movement of his thumb, ' . . . that it's high time you started earning that thirty K I pay you. I'm sending you off on a job.'

'A job?' Jay paled at the word.

'In Hong Kong. I need you to do a spot of tactical gazumping.'

Jay, who had not the least idea how to tactically gazump, or even what it meant, nodded and said 'Yeah, sure. Cool.'

'I've been trying to buy a plot of land in Kowloon which has enormous development potential. It's going to be worth a fortune, once the buildings start going up. Trouble is, just as I thought I was home and dry, a Chinese tycoon muscled in and put in a counterbid. Name's Ping Kee.'

'Pinky,' repeated Jay. 'Sure, I get it. You want me to go out there and put in a higher bid.'

'Exactly. As discreetly and as cheaply as you can.'

'Hey, look,' Jay swigged on his beer, 'I mean, I'm happy to give it a whirl but . . . well, when it comes to wheeler-dealing, you're light years ahead of me. I mean – '

'That's true. But I've got Kawasaki to deal with. And believe me, for all their bowing and scraping, the Japs are far trickier to deal with than the Chinks.'

'Sure,' said Jay. He showed Ivo out, then sank in a heap onto the graphite sofa.

Shit, a job . . .

The phone rang. It was Heidi Plunkett.

'Heyy! Heidi! Have a hip trip? How was deevine LA?'

'Full of people like you, Jay. Look – can I come round? I need someone to talk to . . .'

She sounds tense, thought Jay, but tense women I can handle. Anything seems easy, compared with gazumping Pinky.

'You just missed Ivo,' he told Heidi when she arrived.

'Oh.' she said bleakly.

' . . . And your highlights are growing out. You should get your roots done.'

'Oh, fuck off will you, Jay!'

'All right, all right! Christ, what have *you* got to be so flakey about?'

'I'm sorry.' Heidi stared gloomily at her plimsolls. She took the beer Jay handed her and started to drink from the bottle. 'It's just . . . d'you ever feel that everything in your life is going wrong at once and . . . it's all sort of crowding in on you and squashing you, and – '

'Yeah,' said Jay sympathetically, 'It's like someone beat up on your brain.'

'There's this man in my life and I gave him an ultimatum, only now I'm not sure if I wasn't just cutting off my nose to spite my face, maybe I've only made things worse . . . or maybe there wasn't anything between us anyway, perhaps it was just an illusion . . . like a house of cards, you know – you give it one prod and the whole bloody lot falls down . . . sorry.' She became suddenly self-conscious. 'I'm talking rubbish. Only that's exactly how I feel. As if my head's full of rubbish.'

'Hey, I know,' said Jay. He had draped the grey towel over his head like some bizarre nun's wimple. 'It's like there's this great big garbage can and you just want to tip your life right into it.'

Heidi agreed that was pretty much the size of it.

'It's like in Japan, when the martial arts freaks are preparing for combat. To empty your mind of everything but the fight, you're trained to imagine a big, empty box you're putting all your problems into – like my overdraft for instance – then you picture tipping the box over and throwing it all away . . .' He thought for a moment. ' . . . Japan would really be a great place to go and cool out, wouldn't it. Big brother's heading out there on business for a while.'

At this news Heidi looked even more gloomy.

'Hey, guess what, I'm heading on out to Hong Kong!'

'Brilliant,' said Heidi sourly, 'Another rat leaving the sinking ship.'

'Come with me.'

'No money.'

'Ask Ivo for it.'

'No!'

Heidi looked as though she might break her beer bottle over Jay's head, and he raised his hands in surrender.

'Okay, okay, stay cool! I just thought it would be fun to hang out there together. Like if you and Ivo were in Japan, I could fly out and join you, it's only a couple of hours away and we could – '

'Aren't you forgetting something?'

'What?'

'I'm not going to Japan.'

Jay opened his mouth to speak but thought better of it. Instead he picked up the video remote control and flicked the START switch. 'You on for a re-run of *Mary Poppins?*'

Nine

This is certainly the stupidest thing I've ever done, thought Heidi, as she checked in to Heathrow Terminal One with a gaggle of KGB agents.

She was flying to Tokyo via Moscow, which was not only the cheapest way to arrive but also the quickest. Or so she was informed by Mr Sammy at Jingo Travel, Jay's all-time favourite bucket shop.

'But once you get to Moscow, will they let you out again?' her friends had queried nervously.

' . . . I've heard they overbook the planes so that you have to go without a seat – one guy had to stand all the way from Djakarta . . .'

' . . . Don't they sometimes get as far as Moscow and then pretend there are no onward flights? . . .'

The KGB men were unperturbed. Handsome, in a square-headed way, in ill-fitting, shiny suits, they filled the first-class compartment, cracking Russian jokes with the Aeroflot stewardesses and drinking vodka. All of them removed their shoes and undid their ties.

Heidi, in a cramped second-class seat, wore a Walkman on her head and chewed toffees furiously. It's a business trip, she kept saying to herself over and over, you're going on a business trip. Since her conversation with Jay, she had been unable to get the idea of Japan out of her mind.

Everywhere she turned, she saw posters and books about it. Every other restaurant was a Japanese restaurant. She dreamed about temples and geisha girls. Finally she had gone to Mike Marshall and pleaded with him to let her go to Tokyo to take a look at Japanese game shows. 'Masochism is going to be big ratings, I promise' she had told him.

Mike had agreed reluctantly to let her take the time off, but only if she paid her own way. A refund of her expenses would depend on what she had achieved out there. Heidi had just scraped together enough for a single ticket, and arranged to meet up with Jay, who would lend her the money for a flight back when they eventually decided to return.

I'm only doing this to get myself a promotion, Heidi told herself. It has nothing whatsoever to do with the fact that Ivo Cathcart is in Japan . . .

There was a long wait in Moscow. Heidi marched up and down, her Walkman eyed with suspicion by the armed guard, and disapproval by the fur-wrapped Russian matrons. A small group of Japanese businessmen huddled beneath the DEPARTURE sign, waiting where they were told like obedient children. Only Heidi was prepared to risk Siberia for the sake of stretching her legs. If she exhausted herself, then she would have a better chance of sleeping on the next stage of the journey.

She did sleep, sandwiched between two Suntory-swigging businessmen, and dreaming of graceful temples and picturesque *bonsai*.

At first Heidi thought they had landed in the wrong country. They had left behind a warm, sunny England for a place of teeming drizzle and grey clouds so low they almost touched the tarmac of the runway. She felt dispirited and exhausted. A shiny bright 'skyliner' train was waiting to take the jet-lagged passengers from the airport to the centre of Tokyo, which was apparently over an hour away. The single fare cost Heidi almost a week's spending money.

'*Herro!*' said a voice out of nowhere, once the train was speeding on its way through paddy fields, '*Welcome to Skyriner train . . . we will be arriving in Tokyo in forty minutes. Prease do not forget your berongings.*' The voice on the recorded message, specially chosen for its feminine squeakiness, sounded like a disembodied Minnie Mouse. Heidi obediently disembarked at the central underground station and was rewarded with a pre-programmed '*Have a nice day!*'

Heidi had made no plans, other than arranging a meeting at Japan's chief television network. She had calculated that since Tokyo was a vast cosmopolitan city it would be easy enough to find something to eat and a place to stay. But the underground system was so complex and crowded that it made Piccadilly in the rush hour look like a deserted village street, and everything was so expensive that her precious supply of yen had already dwindled. She wandered her way into Ginza, the main shopping and commercial district. Outside, the streets were a forest of modern skyscrapers. Inside the shopping malls there was floor after floor of seemingly identical shops and restaurants, stretching twelve floors above ground and five floors below. After travelling on a series of escalators, Heidi's spatial awareness and sensory perception began to blur and she could no longer tell where she was going to or where she had been. She had heard of skiers suffering from 'white out'. This was 'shop out'.

Her main priority, despite her rumbling stomach, was finding somewhere to stay, but all the hotels in the Ginza district seemed to start at two hundred pounds a night. When she eventually found someone who understood the words 'Cheaper hotel', she was directed away from the centre of the metropolis to an area where the tower blocks started to merge into nondescript concrete boxes in a tangle of telegraph wires, and indecipherable neon signs in Kanji script. At last there was one Heidi recognised. 'HOTEL' it said, '*Elle & Lui*'. It was a bizarre-looking building, painted pink and purple and shaped like the castle in Walt Disney's 'Sleeping Beauty'.

'I'd like a room please' she said firmly to the desk clerk. The reception area was narrow and dimly lit, with thick purple carpets everywhere, even on the walls.

'Rub hotel,' said the man, bowing profusely. 'Rub hotel.'

'Rub hotel?'

The man nodded. 'Rub hotel.' He was holding out his hand for money.

Obviously it was the custom to pay in advance in Japan. Heidi handed him two hundred yen, which seemed to satisfy him, because he gave her a key and pointed to the lift. The room had more purple carpet and a tiny bed covered with a fake-fur rug. There were mirrors on the ceiling and all around the bed. Nothing looked Japanese except, of course, the prominently placed Mitsubishi video recorder. But it was spotlessly clean and had its own tiny bathroom.

Next on the agenda was something to eat. Heidi dragged herself back towards the city. It was late now, and the salarymen on the trains were drunk on whiskey. They sat slumped in their seats after the train had reached its destination, until white-gloved guards came and bundled them off.

There were restaurants and bars wherever Heidi looked, and they were confusingly similar. Each had its little glass-fronted display cabinet outside the entrance, containing colourful plastic replicas of the food on offer, that the real thing could not possibly live up to.

She ducked inside the bamboo hanging of a traditional bar and was immediately served with green tea and a hot towel sealed in a plastic bag. She ordered suki-yaki, since it was the only Japanese word she knew, and sank gratefully into the shadowy obscurity of the bar. A group of Japanese teenagers ate and drank noisily at a nearby table, but had seen enough *guijin* tourists not to be interested in Heidi. They flashed their cigarettes about and laughed drunkenly in a loud, Western manner. One of their number, a young girl, was crying into her o-sake, wiping her tears with the heated towel. The others ignored her.

'Hey, mind if I join you?'

For a moment, Heidi thought that she was hallucinating and that Jay had joined her already. A tall, skinny figure appeared out of the darkness, dressed in orange loons with preposterous flares and a T-shirt with a picture of a marijuana leaf on it. A blonde Mohican cut stood up from an otherwise tanned skull. Well, thought Heidi, at least he's European.

Her companion whipped out a packet of Rizlas and started rolling a cigarette. 'My name's Stefan. And you? You've only just got here, right?'

Heidi groaned inwardly. It was going to be one of *those* conversations. One in which the old hand outlines the pros and cons to the newcomer at boring length. 'Have you been here long?' she asked. She might as well get the inevitable over with.

'Five years. Came here after Katmandu. Haven't been back to UK since. Wouldn't go back there now. Not to all the fascist repression that poses as a welfare state.'

Stefan's prolonged absence from Britain explained his rather dated air; he was trotting out the same well-worn anarchic clichés that he had taken with him on the hippy trail in 1977. Heidi, eyelids drooping, toyed with her suki-yaki. She was too exhausted even to point out how silly most of his arguments were.

' . . . I mean, we all need space, right? Space to find

ourselves and define our own life-styles . . . where are you staying, by the way?'

'Up the road. Place called the *Elle & Lui*.'

Stefan stared at her incredulously. 'You're not – you've never checked in there have you? In *that* place?'

'Yes, why on earth not?'

'Because it's not a tourist hotel . . . it's a love hotel. Didn't they tell you?'

So that was what the bowing desk clerk had been trying to tell her. *Rub hotel* . . . love hotel.

'It's a place where Japanese couples go to have sex,' Stefan told her, 'Like, they live in really cramped conditions, so they can go off and rent a room for a few hours . . . they provide a video so that you can film the action and then play it back, like "Match of the Day" . . . anyhow, we'll go back there and collect your stuff. You can't possibly stay there.'

'Why not?' asked Heidi coldly. She had been looking forward to falling asleep in her own self-contained capsule.

'Because no-one stays there the whole night – they rent out the rooms by the hour. Don't worry, you can crash out at my pad.'

Stefan's 'pad', predictably, was miles away and involved a long and complicated journey with three changes on suburban trains. Although it was nearly midnight, their carriages were still crowded with men in dark suits. The Tokyo rush hour, it transpired, went on for ever.

The train rushed on through mazes of crooked little wooden houses and impossibly narrow streets, with a glimpse of mountains in the distance. Heidi was no longer feeling, or seeing anything other than a blur of Asiatic features.

' . . . I teach English to the executives of a big Japanese company for four hours a week, that's like my concession to capitalist society. The rest of the time I train in martial arts. It's really a way of expressing your individuality and being totally self-reliant, yet at the same time following ancient tradition. It demands obedience, you know. And you become so . . . *aware*. My kendo teacher has this great philosophy of life.'

'Tell me.' yawned Heidi. Stefan started talking again. She closed her eyes and dreamed of comfortable fake-fur-covered beds surrounded by purple carpet.

'No more oppression!' chanted the members of the North London Women's Sorority, in sing-song voices, 'No more discrimination!'

They were as exuberant as small children at a party, jumping up and down on their coloured bean-bags, their wire-framed glasses steaming over with excitement.

'*Here-we-go, here-we-go, here-we-go!*' they sang, linking arms. '*We are family: I've got all my sisters with me!*'

'Okay, shut up!' Tharka climbed onto a packing case and shouted at the rabble below her. She was dressed in a fringed Indian skirt and a pink sweatshirt that said 'FEMALE GUERILLA'. 'Okay, everyone, stop it! You're behaving like a load of . . . *men!*'

The uproar died down somewhat.

'Just because we've got the final plans doesn't mean we can get hysterical. Right, okay, I'm going to show you the blueprints.'

Tharka unrolled a set of architect's drawings and pinned them up on a blackboard. With a long wooden pointer she began to enumerate details to her avid audience.

'Right – here we have the Self-Awareness Centre. This will comprise a series of studios for yoga, meditation, acupuncture and aromatherapy. And here – ' she tapped a rectangular blob in an authoritarian fashion ' – is the herbalist dispensary. *Now* . . . right over here we have the Lactation Facility for breast-feeding mothers – '

'How are they going to get pregnant?' demanded an earnest young woman with a hennaed crew cut. 'I mean, if no men are allowed within the boundaries – '

'There will be a sperm bank.' Tharka was cold. 'Obviously. Supplies will be brought in from outside.' She looked around the room at the other women, challenging them to find this arrangement unsatisfactory. 'Now, to business. The purpose of our meeting tonight is to decide on a name. So far the site is being referred to as just "The Women's City". But we need something more provocative, something symbolic.'

The women of North London chewed their lower lips.

'How about Feministville?' suggested one.

'Too obvious.'

'Sisterton?'

'Not memorable enough.'

'I know!' cried Robyn Armitage, flushed with triumph, '*Gynberg!*'

Leofred Plunkett's days all began the same way. They all began with a cry of 'Bring on the dummy!'

Six-thirty in the morning, on the set of *Hang-ups*, and the plastic replica of Melodie Ferberger would be taken from the cupboard in the Props Department where she had spent the night. Leofred had grown accustomed to acting opposite a dummy. But to the crew who worked on *Hang-ups*, she was more than part of the scenery, she was a colleague, an idol even. Her strong, silent style of acting had given them a hit show, with all the prestige and financial security that guaranteed, an achievement that did not go unrewarded.

'Hmmm, poor darling, she looks a little peaky today,' said Melvin, the camp Head of Make-Up, resting his hands on silk-shirted hips. 'Never mind sweetie, we'll soon have you fixed. Lindy, pass me Blusher Number 3.'

'Aw, Melvin!' whined Lindy. 'You said *I* could do her make-up today! You know it's my turn!'

'I haven't done her for ages!' chipped in another member of the team.

'For Chrissakes, will you all get out of the way?' The Senior Hair Stylist pushed through the crowd brandishing blow-dryer and brushes. 'I *have* to do something with this wig!'

Leofred sat on the sidelines in his chair marked 'FRED PLUNKETT', thumbing through the scenes that were to be rehearsed that morning. One or two people said a casual 'Hi, Fred' as they walked by, but no-one took much notice of him. He was not the star of the show. The dummy was the star.

As Leofred witnessed the make-up artists and hair sylists fighting over 'Tempest', he felt the stirrings of resentment. He was getting sick of playing second fiddle to a piece of celluloid. Besides, the summer was drawing to a close, and soon he would have to leave the show and return to his studies at Cambridge. The script-writers had already arranged for him to be killed off in spectacular fashion, by a manic machete-wielding patient, jealous of his love for the stoic Tempest. Leofred was forced to contemplate what would follow. His aim had been to impress the trendies of St Godbore's, but would they be impressed if he had been outclassed by a lifeless blow-up doll? Of course not! They would laugh themselves sick.

He reached into his pocket and pulled out a postcard he had just received.

'*Japan is a weird country – weird people, weird food, weird customs. Tomorrow I get my chance to make a mark in the world of international television. Fingers crossed! Heidi.'*

His sister wouldn't tolerate the situation he was in now. She'd tell him not to be so bloody feeble, to get off his backside and start pushing other people around. He racked his brains to try and find some way of making his mark.

As he sat and stared at the script, the answer became obvious. The show was now shot under such pressure that after rehearsal all morning it was broadcast in a live slot. That made everything very simple.

He re-read the script, memorising it.

'Caspar shows the patient out of his office and closes the door behind him.

CASPAR: Tempest, I have to thank you for all the support you've shown. Mrs Friedman is a very difficult patient and I don't think I would have managed her without your help.' . . .

After three hours of rehearsals, the set was made ready. Tempest was propped in her usual chair.

'Okay everyone, we're about to roll. Only twelve seconds until we're on air . . . Fred, on your marker please . . . six, five, four, three, two . . . cue titles! . . .'

After the signature tune had died down, Leofred took the arm of the day player who was Mrs Friedman, and showed her out. Then he strode manfully towards the doll. She smiled at him blankly, as always.

'Tempest, I have to . . .'

He hesitated a second, glancing in the direction of the cameras.

'I . . . I have to say that I'm just as pissed as I could possibly be at your attitude. In fact I'm mad as hell!'

The director waved his arms frantically, calling for a commercial break, but the crew were so transfixed that nobody moved.

' . . . You just sit there, saying nothing! When I ask for your advice, do you give it? – hell no! You just go on staring at me like you want to get laid. You are the dumbest broad I ever met! . . . You're possibly the world's first living brain donor! . . .'

With one fierce movement, Leofred grabbed Tempest's wrist and flung her into the air. He caught her by one of her ankles, waved her round his head like a propeller and sent her flying into the corner, where she landed with her legs wide apart.

'*Cut!*' screamed the director. 'Cut! Plunkett, you're fired!'

Leofred went home to the motel in Santa Monica and took the phone off the hook. All he wanted to do was sleep.

But the sound of a car horn interrupted his dreams. He looked out of the window and straight at a twenty-foot black limousine, sparkling in the sunlight. A grey uniformed chauffeur doffed his cap. Leofred opened the window and leaned out.

'I'm here to take you to the studio, sir.'

'To the studio? But I've been fired . . . are you sure? . . .'

Bemused, he dressed and climbed into the back of the limo. 'I'll come with you if you like, but I think there's been some – '

'You are Mr Plunkett, aren't you?'

'Yes, but – '

'Love your show.' The driver grinned at him in the rearview mirror. 'It's the greatest.'

At the True Life studios, Leofred was met by none other than Byron Ferberger. 'Fred – great to see you!' He wrapped a large oily arm around Leofred's shoulders and led him to his 'office' underneath the artificial sun.

Members of the crew smiled and waved as they passed. 'Hiya, Fred, how ya doing? . . .'

Leofred sat down on a lounger.

'You had breakfast yet?' Byron snapped his fingers. 'Get coffee, on the double! And get me muffins, waffles, maple syrup, bacon. Orange juice. What else d'you eat? . . . I want kippers, and Scotch porridge.'

He leaned back in his chair and rubbed some Hawaian Tropic into his stomach. 'So . . . how much is it going to take?'

'Take?'

'How much – for you to drop your college studies and do another series. The sponsors are crying out for one.'

Leofred swallowed. 'But Mr Ferberger, I sabotaged the show. Live. I thought – '

It was Byron's turn to gulp. 'You mean . . . didn't they call you? I told everyone to call you first thing; my secretary, XYZ's press agent, the assistant producer . . .'

'I disconnected the phone.'

'Oh my God!' Byron shouted to the minion who was bringing a loaded tray of breakfast. 'Get me newspapers, quick! . . . You've made the show even bigger, look!'

'SMASH HIT SENSATION!' cried the *LA Times*, '*Caspar bawls out Tempest!*'

'LIVING BRAIN DONOR SHOCK!' shrieked the *Mirror News*.

'Could I keep these?' asked Leofred politely. Mentally he had already cut them out and pasted them on the wall of his room at St Godbore's. He knew which was his favourite. A large freeze-frame showed Tempest hovering as a blur above his head, with his own features contorted in a primaeval snarl.

'EXCLUSIVE!' it read, 'THE MOUSE THAT ROARED.'

*

'*Duck's gizzards*,' read Jay. 'Hey, that's really incredible. 'Or how about this one – ' He pointed at the menu again. '*Broiled frogs sauté . . . mushed chicken with fish maw . . .* and listen to this one, this is the freakiest of all – *Duck's webs with fish lips . . .*'

Jay Cathcart was sitting in the air-conditioned restaurant of the Peninsula Hotel, Kowloon side. On his left was Gyles Smylie, a representative from Rapier's Hong Kong subsidiary. Gyles was a ruddy-faced young man in a pin-striped suit, fresh from the Scots Guards and the City. He behaved as though they were still in some far-flung corner of the British Empire, clicking his fingers ostentatiously at the Chinese waiters. The waiters scowled at him behind his back and spat into his gin sling.

'Do people actually eat this stuff?' enquired Jay.

'Sure,' said Gyles smoothly, lighting a Marlboro. The family crests on his cuffs gleamed in the pale, haze-filtered sunlight.

'Okay, that's cool.' Jay slammed the menu shut. 'Let's have all of them.'

'Okay, here's the scam,' said Gyles once he had sent the waiters scurrying off to fetch the food, 'Ping Kee's heard on the business grapevine why you're here and he wants a pow-wow. I've set up a meeting between you and him, at his luncheon club.'

'But, I mean, we're about to eat lunch now – won't I be a little late?'

'Just Chink-speak, old chap. Businessmen all belong to these clubs – some of 'em spend all day there. They go to get a bit of tottie, bit of fluff, play mah-jong, smoke opium, eat . . . whatever. Natives, only, naturally. *Quai-loh* – Europeans to you – aren't allowed to join. They can't take the competition. Girls all know we're hung like donkeys compared with the Chinks.' Gyles stabbed his fish lips with a conspiratorial smile. 'So – you go to Central and try and

149

fend off Ping Kee. Then we're all meeting up at Brown's Wine Bar for a swift drinkie, and on to a dinner party in the Mid-Levels.'

'Mid-Levels?' echoed Jay.

'Yah, on the main island. That's where all the *quai-loh* live.'

'Mid-Levels – isn't that kind of . . . mediocre?' Jay was disappointed. 'I always thought it would be really cool to live on the Peak, you know, on top of the heap.'

'No-one lives on the Peak' stated Gyles. 'At least, not People Like Us. Too far, Too touristy. Too damp.'

Jay munched on his duck's gizzards, making a mental note to try as many Chinese delicacies as he could while he was in Hong Kong. It would be a great source of one-upmanship at dinner parties when he got back to London.

Gyles clicked his beefy pink fingers at the waiters.

'Bill!'

They scuttled away, invoking the gods to visit bad luck on all foreign devils.

'Right – got to get back to the office. A word about Ping Kee – he's a slippery old devil. Mixed up with the triads. Treat him bloody carefully or you'll have the little yellow gangsters onto you, know what I mean? Right, see you in Brown's Wine Bar – six-ish.'

Jay took the Star Ferry from the mainland to Victoria and wandered around, trying to find the address that Gyles had given him. The Central business area seeped into the residential districts through a network of twisting roads that wound their way up to the Peak. Rolls Royces glided up Robinson Road to the mid-levels, passing the ubiquitous red taxis with their white gloved drivers, taking rich Chinese women into town to see their brokers. In Queen's Road, where every other building was a bank, the pavements were half obstructed by groups of Chinese staring through the windows at computer screens that displayed the latest share prices. Through open doorways, Jay glimpsed office girls eating lunch at their desks, spreading sheets of newspaper over their work before they started the messy business of shovelling in their Vietnamese noodles.

He made several detours through steep, narrow side-streets full of traditional Chinese steam laundries and dark, dusty spice shops. Everywhere he looked there were people selling: Cartier watches for fifty dollars, personal stereos for twenty dollars, Ray-Bans for ten. Calculating that the heavy, humid sky presaged a storm, Jay bought a telescopic umbrella for fifteen dollars. It fell apart the first time he opened it.

Then it was time for him to negotiate Queen's Road again, dodging the cumbersome blue China Buses and the bright green trams that whistled past him at break-neck speed. Ping Kee's luncheon Club was on the thirty-third floor of a tower block that had not yet been completed. Jay picked his way through girders and rubble only to be told by the immense tuxedo-clad bouncer that men without a tie were not allowed into the club.

Gyles had prepared him for this. He whipped the borrowed bow-tie out of his pocket and clipped it to the collar of his polo shirt. 'Okay?'

The bouncer smiled his most inscrutable smile. 'No jeans, sir.'

'But these aren't ordinary jeans, they're Levis 501s! As seen on TV.'

'Sorry, sir, I do not understand.'

Jay aided his comprehension with a hundred-dollar bill and was admitted with a bow to what looked like a chic European restaurant. Pale, baby-soft carpet deadened the footsteps of the uniformed staff. A barman wielded a cock-tail shaker and poured out Manhattans.

The infamous Ping Kee sat at a round table, surrounded by pretty girls in peacock blue and scarlet cheongsams.

Their gleaming black hair was cut into fashionable Western styles, and they wore make-up. There were coy titters when Jay sat down, and he remembered Gyles' words about the prowess of *quai-lohs*.

'How do you do, Mr Cathcart – I'm Ping Kee. And these are Lily, Mabel, Flora and Tulip.'

The voice was Eton and Oxford, the suit Savile Row. Jay was taken aback, having expected a jibbering, black-clad elder straight from *Enter the Dragon*.

'Fancy a cup of tea?'

'Er . . . sure, why not.'

The tea, when it arrived, was not the thin green Chinese brew but Earl Grey in Minton cups.

'Is this your first time . . . in Hong Kong?' asked one of the girls, and all the others broke into giggles.

Jay blushed like a schoolboy. A small brown hand found its way onto his thigh, a curtain of raven hair brushed dangerously close to his cheek as tea was poured.

'I do like to conduct meetings in earshot of the fairer sex,' said Ping Kee with a charming smile. 'It does brighten them up, wouldn't you say?'

Unfortunately the fairer sex were having a disastrous effect on Jay's already shaky business acumen. Ping Kee discoursed happily for a while on the merits of bespoke tailoring and the Happy Valley race-track, while the girls became ever more friendly, and by the time the conversation was turned to Rapier's bid for the Kowloon land, he could feel the fluttering of small fingers on his leg, his arms, his neck . . . His powers as a negotiator were reduced to nil, his much prized cool had melted. By five o'clock he was actually agreeing to persuade Ivo to reconsider.

With a great effort of will, he tried to stem the tide. 'I'm afraid I have to go now, but I don't feel we can leave things . . .' He pushed his chair away to stop what was going on under the table. ' . . . up in the air. Perhaps we can get together for a bit of a jangle before I leave Hong Kong?'

Ping Kee smiled mysteriously into his Minton cup. 'Perhaps . . .'

It was a relief to escape to the familiarity of Brown's Wine Bar. Here, in the plate-glass luxury of the Exchange Tower, was a little corner of home. Girls with blonde hair and hard faces talked about 'company braychures' in the accents of SW3. They wore neat blouses and skirts and single strands of pearls. Patient Chinese barmen in striped shirts, despising them all, served Beaujolais Nouveau and indifferent Western food.

Still feeling hot under the collar, Jay sat at the bar and ordered a cold beer. A plump, pretty girl with curling, dark hair smiled at him across the room.

Wehay, I'm in there . . .

'Hi!' he said, strolling across to her table.

'We've met, haven't we? At Hugo's dinner party?'

'Fraid not. But listen, I'm in town for a few days and – '

'I thought I knew you,' said the girl. She stopped looking at him and let her eyes flick around the room again. Before Jay could launch a second offensive she had disappeared with a banker in a monogrammed shirt.

His senses still roused by the ministrations of Ping Kee's associates, he turned his attention to the *quai-loh* waitress. Obviously a former student or secretary who had arrived in the colony without the right connections. Or an Australian. Pity her blonde hair was flicked back in that slightly common style, but she was quite good-looking. He made sure his Rolex watch was visible, that would probably impress her.

'Hi, I'm Jay Cathcart . . .'

The sumo wrestler flicked his shining black pigtail over his shoulder. He splashed himself with water, slapped his hands and then his vast, loose belly and squatted down.

'You rike sumo?' enquired Mr Nakarito of Nippon TV, pointing up at the image on the screen. He and Heidi were standing in front of a bank of twelve screens, each playing a different video from the network's library of programmes.

'Ummm . . .' Heidi's mind was reeling with the effort of watching twelve images at once.

'Maybe you rike cookely?' asked Mr Nakarito, pointing to a video of a cookery demonstration. Two Japanese presenters were bowing and scraping while a tall American who spoke very good Japanese taught them how to make Italian lasagne (pronounced rasagne). In the background, a bland and sickly version of *A Time for Us* tinkled away on an invisible piano.

All three presenters picked up a fork to sample the finished product as it came out of the oven. There were 'oohs' and 'ahs' of delight. The camera moved in closer. The lasagne was too hot, and as the camera moved in for a close-up, the American had to spit his out, right back onto his fork. There was a hasty cut to the commercial break.

Heidi burst out laughing.

'Excuse me?' asked Mr Nakarito, baffled by the *guijin* sense of humour. He was a dapper little man in a shiny blue suit, with his company pin on his lapel, like a school badge. 'You rike this one?'

'What I'd really like,' said Heidi, 'is to see some endurance.'

'Ah . . . endorlance.' Bowing rapidly, he led Heidi to another set of screens, all featuring games show contestants in various stages of agony. There was one which particularly appealed to Heidi. The victims had their heads submerged in ice buckets, while above them lighted candles dripped hot wax onto their naked bellies.

'So grotesque, it's wonderful . . .' murmured Heidi with admiration. 'This could be a new cult show in Britain.'

'You rike?'

'Yes, I rike . . . I like this one.'

'You buy?'

'Yes, why not.' Heidi recklessly committed thousands of pounds of TV Mayhem's money. 'And now, could I please use your phone? . . .'

She dialled the number of Jay's hotel in Hong Kong.

'Heyy – what's going down?' said the familiar voice.

'Well, I was rather hoping you were going to tell me that. Have you completed your deal yet?'

'Nope, but I don't give a fuck about that. I'm going to fly out and join you and leave Ivo to clean up the mess.'

'Ivo? Where is he?'

'Still in Kawasaki. But I fancy cooling out on a beach somewhere. A guy here's told me there's a resort called Miyazaki in the south, and he's recommended a hotel called the Blue Lagoon. Meet me there the day after tomorrow.'

'But Jay, I – '

'Don't worry, I'll lend you the dosh.'

'Caller, your time is up, prease!' tinkled the telephone system's own Minnie Mouse.

Heidi hung up with a sigh. She didn't really have any choice but to take the ferry to Kyushu in search of Jay. She didn't have enough money left to get back to England without him. Besides, she had had just about all she could take of Stefan's minimalist life style. He woke Heidi, complete with sake hangover, at six every morning with his Buddhist chanting and would not allow an English tea bag to cross the threshold of his paper-partitioned house.

After saying her farewells to him, Heidi sailed to Kyushu from Kobe on an overnight ferry. It was seven thirty when they docked at the port of Beppu, but already the air was thick with humidity. By the time Heidi's train arrived in Miyazaki at lunchtime, it was quite unbearable.

'MIYAZAKI!' declared the welcoming sign, 'CITY OF GOOD LOOKIN'S'. As the monsoon clouds broke, the good-lookin's were sent racing for shelter. The sound of the rain was so deafening that occupants of the station's phone booths were forced to stick their fingers in their free ear to hear what was being said.

'City of Good Lookin's' was the last English sign that Heidi saw. After that, everything was printed in Kanji script, even the place names. It was late afternoon by the time she reached the Blue Lagoon Hotel. At least the sun's out again, she thought, still time for a swim. The heat was apocryphal. Sweat ran down her back and soaked the waistband of her shorts.

The hotel was deserted except for a wizened, brown man wearing baggy white pants and a chef's cap.

'I'd like a room,' she told him, forcing a smile.

'Brue Ragoon.'

'Yes, I know this is the Blue Lagoon; I want a *room*.'

Of course, he didn't speak English. 'Fukura,' he kept saying; 'Fukura.' He repeated it, pointing at himself, until it dawned on Heidi that he was telling her his name. After much sign language all round, he took her up in the lift to the top floor and deposited her in a Western-style bedroom, despite her insistence that she would be happier with tatami matting and a futon. The Japanese persisted in a belief that *guijin* are not at all adaptable, and quite incapable of sleeping on the floor.

Heidi went into the bathroom and showered off the sweat. The windows were double-glazed, the air-conditioning discreet, and a terrible silence hung about the hotel. She stood still and listened.

There was a creak on the landing.

Wrapping a towel around her naked body, she flung open the door.

Fukura was standing outside, dangerously close to the keyhole.

'*Yes?*'

He grinned, showing blackened stumps of teeth, and started jabbering in Japanese, pointing at the bathroom, then at the carpet that she was dripping all over.

'Look, you stupid little man, you know bloody well I don't speak your language, so why don't you give me a break!'

She slammed the door and waited for the footsteps to retreat. Silence. When she eventually changed into her swimsuit and headed for the beach, Fukura was waiting for her by the lift. He didn't say anything this time, just watched her go, through narrowed eyes. There was still no sign of any other guests.

After she had walked about a quarter of a mile, Heidi found a group of holidaymakers, watched over by lifeguards and a tannoy system playing Japanese rock'n'roll. On the sea wall, an aspiring vandal with a poor grasp of English grammar had sprayed 'I WILL SUCCESS'.

She put her Walkman on her head, clicked in a *Wham!* tape and lay back on her towel to sunbathe. An angry red line was already developing along the edge of her swimsuit. Next to her, an elderly lady sat upright while her middle-aged daughter ceremoniously buried her legs in the sand. Out of the corner of her eye, Heidi watched the mound grow. A large drop of rain fell on it. Then another and another, as a small grey cloud blew in off the sea. The old lady scrabbled desperately to bury her legs as the rain fell faster . . . and faster. The landscape started to disappear. The sand became mud, the sky turned from royal blue to grey-white and eventually merged with the sea in one continuous blur.

The sheets of rain found their way into the mechanics of Heidi's Walkman, turning the *Wham!* boys into Pinky and Perky. Swearing, she wrapped it in her towel and ran back to the Blue Lagoon.

Dressed only in a see-through swimsuit, and with water running off the body in rivulets, it is impossible not to draw attention to oneself. Heidi made a dash through reception to the lift, only to trip over Fukura, who was on his hands and knees brushing the carpet. His eyes travelled upwards and fixed themselves on her breasts, only too visible through her drenched costume.

Once in the sanctuary of her room, she leaned against the door, trembling. Outside, the monsoon rain thundered against the window, while inside the air-conditioning blasted her wet skin, making her shiver. This was terrible. Where the hell was Jay? He should have been there by now, to protect her from the grinning, bowing little man.

She picked up the telephone. Nothing . . . nothing but the faint sound of someone breathing . . . listening.

Heidi slammed the receiver down and tried again. This time there was a line, but the distant receptionist at the hotel in Hong Kong said there was no sign of Mr J. Cathcart, although he did not appear to have checked out yet. In desperation, Heidi asked the operator to try Charles's number in London. No reply.

The silence in the room became overwhelming. She switched on the TV and found an endurance programme similar to the one she had just bought. Feeling reassured, she went into the bathroom and showered off. There was a crunch as she stepped out of the bath-tub.

'Damn, I must have trodden on my . . .'

Under her foot was a two inch cockroach, waving its feelers. Heidi grabbed a towel to flick it away and another cockroach ran from its folds and up her arm. She screamed.

Pressing herself against the wall, she realised that there

was no-one she could ask for help. There was no-one in the whole hotel but her and Fukura, with his gappy, black teeth. Still, there might at least be a can of pesticide in the bedroom. Stepping gingerly over the cockroaches, she reached for the doorhandle . . .

. . . And screamed again. Through the crack in the door, a pair of slant eyes were plainly visible, glistening lasciviously.

She slammed the bathroom door and locked it. 'I'd rather have the cockroaches!' she shouted. 'So you can just go away, you horrible little Nip. Go on – just fuck off!'

She sat on the edge of the bath and looked at her watch. She would wait fifteen minutes and then come out. After five there was a knock that made her jump out of her skin.

'Fuck off, slitty eyes!'

'Hey, what's going on?' said a very un-Japanese voice.

'Jay, thank God!' Wrapping a towel around her, Heidi unlocked the bathroom door.

And fell straight into the arms of Ivo Cathcart.

Ten

Jay Cathcart was spending his last day in Hong Kong at a junk party.

Every wealthy European company in the colony had its own 'junk'. This soubriquet was inspired by the bamboo and wood-structured heaps that were home to thousands of Chinese, but in fact the *quai-loh* junks resembled nothing so much as the gin palaces that cruise the River Thames. And a weekend junk party was like a floating house-party, with a dozen or so braying young bloods setting sail into the South China Sea to get plastered and wallow in in-humour.

Gyles Smylie took Jay down to the Queen's Pier, where battle was to commence. A row of gleaming white junks was lined up at the landing stage, complete with their crew of Chinese boat-boys, whose job it was to cater to the whims of the guests. Jay was introduced, amid the rounds of jaw-clashing, to the nine other cosmonauts, and the junk chugged out across the dark, calm water, winding its way between hummocky green islands.

Drinks were served immediately. The old hands opted for gin or red wine, their stomachs hardened by regular junk outings. Jay ordered lager, unsure of the effect that the ground swell was having on his stomach. He lay back on the top deck with his eyes closed and let the sun get on with its all-important work. Imagine returning to England without a sun-tan . . .

After the boat boys had been around with a tray of drinks, Gyles cornered Jay on the sun deck. 'Listen, I don't believe you're really going to fly out to Japan tonight to see your bit of tottie and leave the Ping Kee bid still standing! We were all rather hoping you were going to muscle the old bugger out, I must say.'

Jay lowered his Ray Bans over his eyes with a shrug. 'Hey, I mean, what can I do? I tried calling his office, but they wouldn't put me through.' He sat up to take a sip of his iced beer and then lay down again. 'It's the lot of the international businessman. You win some . . . you lose some.'

'Well, I must say I admire your cool, but . . . Good God!' Gyles snatched up the binoculars that were hanging around his neck. 'Talk of the bloody yellow devil! . . . That's Ping Kee's yacht over there!'

It gleamed on the horizon, a hundred-and-fifty feet long, its pure whiteness punctuated with black dots that turned out, as the yacht grew closer, to be armed security guards.

' . . . There's someone coming over. Look!' One of Ping Kee's crew had climbed into a speed boat and was coming towards their junk. Gyles hurried over to the steps and took the message that the crewman was holding out.

'It's for you!' he shouted at Jay's prone figure. 'Will you do Mr Ping Kee the honour of joining him on his yacht for some light refreshment? . . .'

The outboard motor bounced across the swell of the waves in an undignified fashion, and by the time Jay arrived alongside Ping Kee's yacht he was feeling nauseated and uncool. His green complexion was spotted immediately by his host, who stood at the top of the landing steps with a reception committee of Chinese beauties.

'Mr Cathcart, how very decent of you to come!' he said

in his clipped Etonian accent. He wore a large silk cravat tucked into the neck of his shirt and a ridiculous peaked yachting hat. 'You look very much as if you're in need of refreshment. Do come into the salon.'

Jay staggered after him into a huge cabin that was decorated with a lot of gilt and marble and yellow silk drapes.

'A Bloody Mary would be the thing, perhaps?' asked Ping Kee. He snapped his fingers and a tray appeared bearing a tumbler of ice-cold, brownish liquid. Jay took a tentative sip and felt his stomach rebel. Beads of sweat broke out on his forehead. 'Hey, look, Mr Pinkie, I mean, while I'm here I might as well – '

'I find that a massage is a very good cure for sea-sickness,' Ping Kee's narrow eyes glittered. 'Perhaps you'd like to try it?' He snapped his fingers again, summoning a lithe young woman in a pair of white silk pyjamas.

'No, really, I . . .' protested Jay as her nimble fingers pulled his shirt from the waistband of his shorts, 'I just came to – '

'I should just enjoy it, if I were you.' observed Ping Kee sagely. 'You'll soon be feeling much better.'

He was right. Within seconds Jay found himself semi-naked lying face down on a white sofa while the magical brown fingers probed his flesh. The sensation was nothing short of miraculous. As Ping Kee had predicted, the nausea was soon dispersed, and replaced by feelings of a quite different nature, as feminine fingers fluttered around the nape of his neck, and the base of his spine.

His host stood and watched the procedure with some satisfaction, surrounded by his chorus of giggling beauties. 'Now that you're feeling refreshed, Mr Cathcart . . .'

Jay groaned.

' . . . We have an ideal opportunity to discuss your brother's bid on the Kowloon land.'

Jay groaned again.

' . . . Only, I seem to remember that at our last meeting you mentioned advising your brother to abandon his bid . . .'

'Uuhhh . . . I . . .'

'Perhaps you would be prepared to consider this course of action more seriously?'

Jay's brain turned to jelly as the fingers swarmed beneath his hips and towards his groin. 'Yeah . . . sure, why not?' he heard himself saying. Only part of him was paying attention to Ping Kee, anyway. The rest of him was concentrated below the waist.

'Excellent.' Ping Kee snapped his fingers and, the massage stopped abruptly. The blood began to rush back to Jay's head. 'Shall we get something down in writing?'

Jay sat up and the Bloody Mary rushed up his gorge and into his mouth. His nausea returned and so did his sanity.

'Er, look, forget it, right?'

'Forget it?' Ping Kee narrowed his eyes again.

'That's what I said.' Driven more by the desire to hang his head over the side of a lavatory pan than by a new-found ruthlessness he went on, 'There's no way my brother's going to be pissed about over this. If you go higher, he'll just bring in a consortium of other companies to muscle you out . . . now where's that bloody rowing boat of yours?'

Jay left his Bloody Mary in the South China Sea and returned to his own junk, pale, but heroic.

'Piece of piss,' he told his impressed fellow passengers. 'I just told the little yellow man where to get off. He can't push Rapier Industries around as if they were some tin-pot little company.'

Only Gyles sounded a note of caution. 'Good job you're leaving tonight, though. I expect Ping Kee's hopping mad that you're not backing out after all. I wouldn't put it past him to play dirty – far from it.'

163

There were murmurs of agreement at this. 'Check your suitcase for bombs *before* you get to Kai Tak airport . . .'

The trip was drawing to a close. The patient boat boys served tea with wafer-thin biscuits from Fortnum and Mason, and then started up the engines for the cruise back to Queen's Pier. Jay heaved an inward sigh of relief.

Once they were on dry land, he said goodbye to Gyles for the final time.

'Straight off to the airport, is it, to fly off and join your bit of fluff?'

'Got a bit of time to kill first. Thought I'd cruise off and find some food . . .'

Instead of the upmarket restaurant district in Causeway Bay, Jay took a taxi to insalubrious Aberdeen where the lumbering three-storey floating restaurants were moored in a smelly harbour amongst Chinese sam-pans and the yachts of the wealthy *quai-loh*. Coloured lanterns bobbed against the side of the restaurants, guiding the tourists who arrived in their hordes across the darkened waters, eager for their crispy spring rolls and their Peking Duck.

Jay was intrigued, but decided that he was looking for a far more esoteric culinary experience, a taste of the real Hong Kong. He fought his way through shopping streets ablaze with neon, where traders were still doing their best to make a hundred dollars for a fake Gucci bag, and on into the more arcane back alleys where old Haklo men and women in traditional dress stirred murky pans of cat and dog meat over paraffin burners. The heat from these burners was fierce; adding to the warmth in the humid night air, and Jay was wet all over with sweat. He ducked into a small cafe, all bare formica and fluorescent lights.

'Beer, please!' he shouted to the waiter who was scurrying between the small tables. 'Make it a cold one.'

There were no other *quai-lohs* in the restaurant, but plenty of dingy Chinese holding their bowls close to their mouths and scooping greedily. This excited Jay's sense of adventure, he ran his eye down the menu, an expert after only a few days in Hong Kong.

'Hmmm . . . "Fish lips"; had that already . . . "Duck's gizzards"; had that too . . . hey, this is a new one: "Chef's Special – Blowfish" . . .'

He waved at the waiter. 'I'll have the blowfish, please.'

The waiter broke into a voluble stream of Cantonese, gesturing with his hands and becoming very excited. Several of the kitchen hands joined in, with giggles and glottal cries of exclamation.

' . . . And don't be all night about it, I've got a plane to catch.'

About fifteen minutes later, a steaming plate appeared, heaped with slices of what looked like mottled purple rubber. The waiters stood around watching as Jay forced it down, smacking his lips with satisfaction. In fact its taste was acrid and revolting, but Jay had become familiar with the Asian concept of loss of face and was anxious not to lose his.

His Rolex told him that unless he got a move on, he was going to be late for check-in. And he still had to call at his hotel and collect his luggage. He hurried down the alleyway, checking over his shoulder for the reassuring sight of a red taxi cab, but there were none around. He turned into another narrow street, then another . . . but in each there were only the blazing paraffin burners, spewing out their oppressive heat. No car of any description penetrated them.

Jay wiped the sweat from his forehead and set off again in search of the main street, unaware that he was being followed.

Not only was he as hot as hell, but starting to feel dizzy and out of breath. He stopped and looked back up the steep alley. He was confused. Were there two men standing there, watching him, or was he imagining things? . . .

A few minutes later, Jay Cathcart's body lay motionless in a gutter with a thin stream of blood trickling from his open mouth.

'What the hell are you doing here?' Heidi demanded, although secretly she was pleased to see Ivo.

He looked damp and dishevelled in his suit and tie, and when he removed his jacket there were dark circles of sweat under the arms of his shirt. He sank wearily onto the edge of the bed and switched off the TV, which was still spouting endurance games.

' . . . More to the point,' Heidi continued, 'how did you know *I* was here?' She snatched up another towel and started to rub her short hair until it stood up from her scalp in spikes.

'Jay told me,' said Ivo, picking up the telephone receiver. ' . . . How the hell do you get room service in this god-forsaken place? Hello? . . . Hello? . . . *mushi mushi* . . . I want a gin and tonic please, with plenty of ice . . . no, *gin* and *tonic* . . . Oh, Christ, what's the point?!' He slammed down the phone.

'That's just typical of Jay!' Heidi was seething. 'He can go round blabbing to you about where I am, but he can't even show up here when he's supposed to!'

'That's Jay I'm afraid; utterly unreliable. I, on the other hand, am completely unwavering. So you'd better have dinner with me tonight, instead.'

Ivo had checked into the Blue Lagoon, and in accordance with the national perversity had been given a Japanese room when he wanted a Western-style one.

'All this sleeping on the floor rubbish,' he complained. 'I've had enough of it.'

'Your problem is that you're completely inflexible,' observed Heidi, 'I suppose that's the reason for your grossly over-inflated success.'

They were sitting in Ivo's room, being served dinner. Not – to Heidi's relief – by the lecherous Fukura – but by an elderly lady in traditional kimono. They sat cross-legged on the tatami, wrapped in their blue and white *yukata*, the wide-sleeved cotton robes provided for all guests at inns and hotels. A complex series of lacquer bowls and trays was being laid out on the low table.

' . . . and another thing that gets on my nerves,' said Ivo, as the waitress retreated backwards with her nose virtually touching her white socks, 'is this continual bowing and scraping. It makes me feel uncomfortable.'

Ivo couldn't cope with the East. For the first time, Heidi was seeing him unable to control his environment, and she was relishing it. She pressed raw fish on him and he shuddered, she offered him chunks of cold egg wrapped in seaweed and he curled his lip.

'Dear God, that place – Kawasaki!' he groaned, emptying the contents of a sake bottle down his throat in one go. 'The Sunderland of Japan. Imagine a refinery the size of Los Angeles and you've got Kawasaki. Endless rows of factories and sweat-shops. Christ, we hear all these glowing reports of industrial management in Japan, and yet they still have sweated labour. Thousands of people toiling away sticking micro-chips together! Who would have thought it of the goody-goody Japanese? This is another world all right. I felt like Marco bloody Polo!'

'Perhaps we should expect it,' suggested Heidi, licking soy sauce from her fingers. 'That the most fascinating country in the world is also the most exasperating. Well, that's my verdict, anyway.' She gulped her sake in an unfeminine fashion.

'For once we agree about something! I tell you, in all my years as a businessman I've never had such a hard time. It's not that they're aggressive, it's quite the opposite. They don't respond to aggression. I'm used to getting things done by throwing my weight around, but here the response to bad temper is just more nodding and bowing!'

The waitress crept in to clear away the food and pour green tea. They drank it in silence.

'You're going to have to get me out of this place,' Heidi said suddenly. Ivo looked at her hard, and she felt her face going red. It really was demeaning to be in this position, after turning down race-horses and yachts and ripping up cheques for six figures.

' . . . I don't have any money left,' she explained. 'And I was going to borrow some from Jay, to pay for my ticket home. Only Jay hasn't showed up.'

Ivo sat intensely still, just staring at her. The only movement was a quivering of his pig-like nostrils and the flickering of his eye-balls as he looked first at her face, then at her crossed legs, then up to her breasts.

'I won't lend you the money,' he said eventually. 'I'll give it to you. Enough for a first-class ticket home. On the condition that you sleep with me.'

His audacity took Heidi's breath away.

I should have known. I should have realised that he wouldn't give up until he'd got me cornered . . .

They knelt opposite one another over the low table, like two samurai about to go into combat. 'I refuse,' said Heidi, pouring herself some tea. 'You have a reputation for being completely ruthless, but even you wouldn't fly out of here and leave me stranded. I could always telephone the *News of the World* . . . '

Ivo shrugged. 'You can call my bluff, if you like. But a

story in the papers would increase interest in my Japanese venture. Might even raise the share price a few points.'

Heidi ground her teeth in fury. She did not want to risk being stuck in this godforsaken town, and he knew it. 'All right,' she said. 'I'll go to bed with you.'

. . . *But don't expect to enjoy it, buster! Because I'm going to make sure you don't* . . .

Quick as a flash, Ivo jumped to his feet and pulled a rolled-up futon from behind the sliding partition.

'Oh no,' said Heidi. 'You don't get your payment now. Not until I'm booked on my flight. No ticket, no sex.' She sauntered to the door. 'I'll see you in the morning. Have your credit cards at the ready.'

When Heidi rose at nine the next morning, Ivo already had a taxi waiting to take them from Aoshima to Miyazaki. He didn't even give her time to swallow her Japanese breakfast of cold fried egg and pickled seaweed. She climbed into shorts, T-shirt and flip-flops and allowed herself to be bundled into the back of the taxi.

' "MIYAZAKI – CITY OF GOOD LOOKIN'S" ' Ivo read the sign as they passed it. 'Dear God, can you believe these people?'

He paid the taxi driver, who had pointed them to a travel agent on the other side of the main street, next to a department store. They waited at a pedestrian crossing while hundreds of pastel-coloured Datsuns and Nissans hurtled past. The signals to wait or to cross were not controlled by coloured lights, but by two different computerised melodies.

'What if you don't recognise the tune?' wondered Ivo.

'You end up being pancaked by a baby-pink hatchback.'

Ivo shepherded her across, steering her protectively through the hordes of Japanese commuters. Heidi rather enjoyed the touch of his hand on her bare arm; then remembered the reason they were going to the travel agent together, and felt furious.

To the strains of the theme from *Gone With the Wind* on the inevitable muzak system, Ivo flashed his gold credit card and was handed a first-class JAL ticket from Osaka to Heathrow.

'Quicker than going from Tokyo,' he said.

'Great.' Heidi snatched the ticket and put it in the pocket of her shorts. 'Shall we go back to the Blue Lagoon and get on with it?'

'What – now?'

'Yes, why not?' Heidi pulled out the ticket and examined it. 'If we go back now, that'll just allow me enough time to get to Miyazaki Airport in time for the lunchtime connecting flight.'

'But . . . Heidi, for God's sake, it's only eleven in the morning. I mean, I thought at least we might – '

She swung round to face him. 'As I recall, there was nothing in our agreement that stipulated what time of day it had to be. Come on . . .'

When the taxi arrived at the Blue Lagoon, Heidi marched Ivo straight through the foyer and into the lift.

'Right,' she said briskly, when they reached the fourth floor. 'Get your trousers off. I hope you're feeling horny.' She unwrapped a piece of chewing gum and popped it in her mouth.

'But – '

Heidi wrenched back the sliding doors in Ivo's room and dragged the futon out onto the tatami.

'Er . . . perhaps we'd be better off in your room, in the normal bed.'

'Sorry, it's the futon or nothing.'

Ivo went into the bathroom and emerged wearing his *yukata*. The square contours of the robe made him appear even stockier than usual. His already pink face had caught the sun, and there was an angry purpley line where his porcine head emerged from the neck of the robe. An attempt had been made to slick his hair down with water. All in all, he looked faintly ridiculous.

Heidi was lying in wait on the futon. She wore a T-shirt and a pair of white cotton knickers, but her legs and stubby feet were bare. Her jaw worked away rhythmically on the piece of gum. A pair of stereo headphones adorned her head, making a faint buzzing sound as Bruce Springsteen sang into her ears.

When she saw Ivo, she switched off the Walkman and removed the headphones. 'Okay, let's go.' She lay on her back with her eyes closed and her jaw still moving, like some bizarre human sacrifice.

Ivo stared down at her. He stared at her girlish white underpants, at the outline of her small jutting breasts, like puppy dogs' noses . . . at her infinite vulnerability.

'It's all right,' he said. 'You win.'

She opened one eye and peered up at him. 'What?'

'I said "you win". I don't want to do it.'

'Does that mean I'm stuck here?'

Ivo sighed. 'No . . .' He picked up the ticket and dropped it on her stomach. 'It's all yours. Have a good trip.'

Charles Jolyon was at home in Primrose Hill, enjoying a rare moment of peace.

His children had just been dragged kicking and screaming to school by the au pair. He could hear her grinding the gears of the Volvo as she shot down the road, narrowly missing the front wing of a neighbour's BMW. Joy had claimed she had some shopping to do and had gone off in search of six-packs of pantyhose, or the perfect washing powder or whatever it was that she needed to run her life properly.

Charles sat at his desk in the study, contemplating the future. He was at the mid-life crossroads, and there were two directions in which he could go. One was sign-posted 'More of the Same'. More intermittent squabbles with Joy, more thrice-yearly sex (New Year's Eve, August Bank Holiday and his birthday), more futile attempts at disciplining his children. More of the au pair's pubic hairs in the bath. The other direction, signposted 'Heidi Plunkett', was something of an unknown quantity.

On the desk in front of him was a buff envelope full of old photographs. He pulled out a few and examined the battered images. A picture of himself as a student, dressed in duffle-coat, turtle neck and winkle pickers, carrying an armful of hip and meaningful books. Then came Charles Jolyon, the ambitious young television executive, sitting astride a 500cc motorbike in a leather jacket. He had loved that bike, but he'd sold it to buy Joy a fitted kitchen. There was a picture of a heavily pregnant Joy standing in front of a 'Maternity Admissions' sign, wearing a flowered smock and a beaming smile. And his children, at an age when they were still tractable, staring up at a Christmas tree with glowing eyes.

These emotive images of his own past enveloped him in a mantle of security. They weren't perfect; in many ways they were very ordinary, but what they represented was familiar and fathomable. The devil he knew. Heidi, on the other hand, was nothing if not unpredictable. She would probably leave him in two years' time for a younger man. She couldn't cook, and had no interest in housekeeping at all. He shuddered as he thought of her room in Grafton Road, with its empty beer cans and underwear smeared across the carpet. Was that really what he wanted? Or would he not be a lot more comfortable in his marital disharmony with Joy?

He turned over the dilemma in his mind as he travelled on the Underground to work, but the nearer he got to TV Mayhem, the more impossible it was to see Heidi in anything but the most negative light. He dwelt on her sullenness, her flashes of bad temper. Her stubbornness, her scruffiness. Even her youth had suddenly lost its appeal. She's too immature to ride the ups and downs of a relationship, he told himself. She's just a kid.

In his office, the usual level of Monday morning chaos had built up. It was Charles' habit to arrive late, at about ten thirty, so that a sense of urgency had been guaranteed and the list of calls to return had been allowed to grow. It gave him a sense of importance to have everybody looking for him.

Megan, his secretary, bustled in with an armful of files.

'We have a crisis,' she declared. 'Over the Fanny Craddock interview. Also, that feature on the proliferation of Lebanese supermarkets in Hammersmith. Apparently some footage has gone missing and everybody's denying responsibility.'

Charles sighed. 'So what's new?'

'And I'm to give you this – ' Megan thrust a sheaf of papers under his nose. 'From Heidi Plunkett. Transcripts of the Cathcart interviews. She said Mike Marshall needs to know if you want any more.'

'You mean – she's back?' Charles sounded nervous. 'I thought she was going to be away another week.'

'Apparently her travel plans didn't quite work out as she'd hoped. Do you want to see her? . . . I could send her to Mike . . .'

Charles gave a deep sigh and buried his head in his hands. 'No, send her in.'

Heidi sauntered in five minutes later looking very . . .

Charles racked his brains for the right word and could only come up with 'cute'. She was tanned, and her hair, still sporting golden streaks from her trip to the Beverly Hills beauty parlour, had been scraped up into a jaunty little coxcomb of a ponytail. The length of her hair was inadequate for this purpose, which Charles found hopelessly touching. She wore tight white leggings and a black T-shirt with no bra underneath.

'Oh, Heidi . . .' The tone of his voice was grave and despairing, but his body was propelled by an independent and baser force. He crossed the room in one stride and grasped Heidi in a greedy embrace, kissing her forehead, eyelids and nose and finally clamping her jaw in a wet kiss. Heidi gave in with good grace, moulding her body against his.

'So,' she said finally, wiping her mouth with the back of her hand where he had drooled over her. 'You've decided!'

'Yes, I have.' Charles returned to his desk, wiping the steam from his spectacles. 'I'm afraid I've decided, Heidi, that I must stay with my wife.'

'For how long?'

'I don't think you quite understand, Heidi. I meant that I intend to stay with her permanently.'

'But I thought – '

'Believe me Heidi, it's not for my sake. It's not . . .' He issued a dramatic sigh. ' . . . It's not what *I* want at all. But you see, I can't afford to think of my own happiness. I have to think of the children. I have to think of Joy, who would be absolutely . . . destroyed if she had to struggle through life on her own. In short – ' He gave a brief, martyred smile, 'What we're talking about here is sacrifice.'

Heidi, who had paled a little during this moving speech, gave a snort of derision. 'I can't really argue with that, can I? I'm not even going to try. So let's talk business instead. First – Japan. I'm writing up a report of my trip and I shall need your approval for a programme purchase I think we should make. Also I need your signature on my expense claim form . . .' She went on rapidly without looking at his face, 'Secondly, I've done the last scheduled interview in the Cathcart series, but Mike and I think we might need more material.'

'Ah, yes . . . obviously under the circumstances it will be impossible for you and I to work together. I'm going to arrange for you to be transferred to the Cookery Department. They need a researcher on their new afternoon show, "Vegan Party".'

'And the Cathcart job?'

'If it does need more work, I'll ask Mike to send someone else to Rapier to finish it. I think – '

Heidi executed her biggest slam yet with the door of Charles' office. The frame cracked and splintered at the hinges, and the twin towers of TV Mayhem were rocked to their foundations.

Heidi returned to Grafton Road at seven thirty in a black and bloody mood.

She still hadn't completed her unpacking after her return from Japan, and her case lay open on the floor, vomiting forth its contents. She aimed a kick at the case and threw a handful of clothes around the room. The London phone directory (section A to K) was ripped and thrown against the purple wall.

Feeling calmer, she sat down on the edge of the bed and went through her mail. A credit card bill, a phone bill, junk mail and a postcard from Josie on her honeymoon.

'WONDERFUL VIEWS OF THE HOTEL BATH-ROOM AS I SPEND TWENTY-FOUR HOURS A DAY

She went through the pile again, hoping to find something from Jay, or even Ivo, but there was nothing. It occurred to her then that her rage was not so much due to Charles' marital consolidation as to her removal from the Cathcart job. In renewed frustration, she hurled her teddy bear across the room, where it landed next to the ripped telephone directory.

'Shit, shit, SHIT!'

She picked up the phone and punched in a London number, but chickened out before it began to ring. Groaning, she lay back on the bed and closed her eyes.

The phone rang, making her jump out of her skin.

'Heidi. It's Ivo Cathcart.'

It was like telepathy. She was too stunned to speak.

'I'm afraid I've got some bad news about Jay.'

'What's wrong? I've tried to ring him, but – '

'He's in hospital.'

'*Hospital?*'

'Don't worry, he's going to be all right. It happened in Hong Kong. He was poisoned.'

'My God, who poisoned him?'

Ivo laughed. 'It's a very long story. I think I'd better let him tell you. I'm going to the hospital now, and I'm taking you with me.'

'Where are you?'

'Look out of the window.'

Heidi did. The white Bentley Continental was parked outside in Grafton Road. Ivo was talking to her on the car phone.

' . . . Not exactly inconspicuous, are you?' she said as she slipped into the back seat beside him. 'I mean, you're never going to catch anyone out as long as you arrive in this thing.'

Jay was a patient at the private Cashrich Clinic in the Cromwell Road. Heidi sniffed the air as she entered. 'I've never been in one of these places before. Not the same without the regulation NHS disinfectant, is it?'

Several Arabs in long robes and red and white tablecloths were roaming around the brightly lit foyer. A group of nurses, with glossy blonde manes and manicured nails, leaned against the reception desk, gossiping and laughing.

Jay was housed in what looked like a private Chapel of Rest, his bed surrounded by grotesquely large flower arrangements. 'Hey, get down!' he said, with a weak grin. 'Oh . . . *you're* here.' He saw Ivo behind Heidi.

The patient made rather a pathetic figure in his hospital gown, denuded of his status symbols. Without the flashy car, the gold Rolex watch and the Gucci loafers, he hardly seemed like Jay at all.

'Hey, Heidi, look at this!' He pressed a switch on the side of the bed and it lowered itself into a semi-prone position. 'First gear . . .' He pressed it again and it went lower. ' . . . Second. Cool isn't it? I've got a turbo-charged bed.'

Heidi sat down beside him and helped herself to a martini glass full of Lucozade. 'So, what happened?'

Jay leaned back on his pillows and groaned. 'Blowfish? How was I to know that it's lethal unless it's prepared properly? You need a special licence to serve it, and of course the place I went to didn't have one. And there was I thinking "Wow, this is a really new taste sensation!" Five minutes later the lining of my stomach had started to bleed. It would have been "Bye bye Jay" time if a couple of tourists hadn't come down the same street and found me unconscious . . . so it was a quick session with the old stomach pump, then time to call in the boys from BUPA and hitch a ride home in an air ambulance.'

'Jay, you wally!'

'I know, I know . . .'

'I'm sure it won't be long before he's back to his old self again,' Heidi said as they left the hospital. She spoke a trifle primly, conscious that Ivo's hand was in the small of her back guiding her down the steps.

'Idiots like my brother have at least twenty lives.' Ivo's tone was resigned. 'He'll soon be back to wasting all my money. Anyway, did you see the gang of brainless girl-friends queuing up outside the door when we left?'

He came to a halt on the step below Heidi and turned round to face her squarely. 'So, how about you and me? I think it's about time we . . . got our act together.'

She folded her arms over her chest. 'You really are incredible! You still think you can buy me?' Pound signs flashed in her brain and she did some hasty calculations. The price had come down, and was falling.

'Oh no, this won't be an acquisition. At least, not a straight cash transaction. I'm going to leave my wife.'

Heidi laughed in his face. 'Really? Well, I'm afraid you'll have to excuse me . . .' She steered herself away from the car door that was being held open for her, ' . . . but you see, I've heard that line before. Someone's already tried it on me. And it didn't work.'

'Have a nice day's shopping, darling?' Charles Jolyon heard the front door slam. 'I must say, it's taken you a long time.'

Joy/Tharka came into the kitchen. 'What the hell are you doing?' she demanded.

Her husband was swooping around the kitchen in a frilly apron. In one hand he held a fistful of carnations and gypsophila which he was cramming into a vase, in the other a bottle of champagne. The table was set for two, with candles and matching napkins – linen, not paper. Several saucepans were bubbling away on the Aga, and there was a board covered with a grey, lumpy substance on the worktop.

'What's that?'

'Ah . . . pastry for the Beef Wellington. Listen darling – '

Joy was scowling. 'And what's this in aid of? Have you got some fancy piece coming to dinner? Poor cow!'

'No, no! It's for *you*! I'm cooking dinner for you, as an expression of my appreciation. The kids are in bed. Helga's gone out with the boy from the Greek delicatessen. It's just you and me . . . Is that what you bought? Let me see.'

Charles pointed to the carrier bags at Joy's feet. She took out a pile of identical T-shirts and held one of them against her chest. It was white, with red and black printing on it.

'Very nice, darling . . . *GYNBERG '87* – is that some Rhineland town we bombed in the war? . . . And what's it got to do with that man with . . . oh . . . oh my God, it's a picture of a man with his prick cut off! Good God Joy, did you realise that when you bought it? Don't tell me you went all the way to Brent Cross for – '

'Gynberg is where I'm going. Me and the kids.'

'You're taking them on holiday? That's nice – '

'No. I mean I'm leaving you.'

Charles dropped the soup ladle onto the floor, where it splashed a dark green spray of watercress over his trousers.

'Sit down, Charles.'

'Bloody hell, Joy! I mean, Christ – '

'*Sit down!*' snarled Tharka in a voice her husband didn't recognise. He obeyed.

She shrugged the T-shirt on over what she was wearing, and adopted the authoritarian style of delivery she employed with the Women's Sorority. 'Gynberg is a new town, near Milton Keynes. Only it's a new town with a difference.'

'There's nothing different about a new town having a daft name.' Charles' tone was flippant. 'I mean, look at Ashby-de-la-Zouche, Welwyn Garden City – '

'Look at *this* will you!' said Tharka fiercely, tapping the picture of the castrated man, who cowered in the valley between her breasts. 'It's a city without men. None are allowed to live within its boundaries. Or even to cross them.'

'Not even the postman?'

'We will have postwomen, of course. We will be self-sufficient in every way, a community for the eighties.'

Charles was bewildered. 'But when did this happen? You never said . . . I thought . . .'

'It's been going on for months. Only you never noticed.'

'Er . . . who are you going with?'

'With the other members of my women's collective. And with Thaddeus and Clytemnestra, of course. They will be re-educated according to non-aggressive, pacifist, non-sexist – '

'*Non-sexist!* This is just about the most outrageous piece of sexism I've ever witnessed! It's a fucking conspiracy! I suppose Helga's going, too!'

'She wouldn't last five minutes without the sight of a well-filled crotch!' said Tharka scornfully. 'You can keep her!'

She gathered up the T-shirts and swept out of the kitchen to pack.

Charles poured himself a large measure of cooking brandy. Then another. After three brandies, he was galvanised into action. Of course, this was the best thing that could possibly have happened. It would have looked a bit off for him to walk out on his wife and kids, but now that it had happened to him, no-one could point the finger. No-one could say that he had dodged his responsibility to his children.

He shuddered at the thought of Thaddeus being brought up amongst all those ball-breaking feminists. Heidi wouldn't go in for that sort of nonsense. Heidi was a *real* woman. She knew how to make a man feel masterful. Potent. Sure, she was scatty and untidy, but that was appealing. Besides, when she moved in here with him, they could get a cleaning lady to pick up after her. Helga would have to go, but that was no loss.

Filled with brandy and a sense of everything being for the best in the best of all possible worlds, he picked up the phone and dialled Heidi's number. It was engaged. Undeterred, he dialled again.

Ivo Cathcart was speeding towards Hampshire, and his elegant country mansion. He was not, as usual, in the fat, white Bentley, but in the back of a taxi. Heidi's remark about the obvious style of his vehicle had cut deep, and today he had a particular wish to be incognito. He was about to prove a point, to himself and to the world at large. He was going to prove that Linda didn't need him at all. And to do that, he had to catch her unawares.

The cabbie dropped him at the bottom of the drive. Ivo gave him a fifty-pound note and told him to wait. He had never walked up his own driveway before, and hadn't realised quite how long it was. Nor had he ever noticed the colourful profusion of shrubs that grew along its border.

Inside, the house was silent, except for the low hum of the vacuum cleaner wielded by the Filipino maid. She glanced at him suspiciously, not recognising him. The children were no doubt secreted in the distant recesses of the nursery with their Norland nanny.

There were signs of Linda's presence in the drawing room. Clues. A glossy magazine open on a white sofa. A pair of Manolo Blahnik shoes kicked off on the rug. An ashtray with a lipstick-smeared butt. A wineglass . . . two wineglasses.

Ivo's gaze was drawn to the French windows, which stood slightly open, admitting the brilliant afternoon sun. The lawn sloped away about fifty yards to a rose border, and beyond that, a tennis court. He could make out Linda's slim figure, dazzling in her whites, her blonde ponytail flicking around her shoulders as she volleyed from the net.

She was partnered by her tennis coach, Bruce Wise, a brawny young man with dark, hairy forearms. The game ended and Linda ran up to the net. So did Bruce Wise, only he gripped it with his hairy hand and vaulted over it. Linda was enfolded in a sweaty embrace. She dropped her racket. And her balls.

Ivo turned away from the window. He had seen enough. The same sterile silence persisted inside the house. That alone was enough to tell him that his presence had no influence. He took his cheque book from his jacket pocket and wrote out a cheque for a million pounds, payable to Linda. '*The down payment on your divorce settlement.*' he scribbled on the back, and left it on the coffee table beside the glasses of wine.

The taxi sped away from the house and up the lane.

'Stop!' shouted Ivo, as they approached the village. 'Pull in here. I need to make a call.'

He went into the phone booth by the side of the road. It stank of urine and stale cigarette smoke and was decorated with uninspiring grafitti. '*SCREW MAGGIE*' Ivo read, '*FUCK THE FALKLANDS.*' 'SHOOT THE POPE.'

He picked up the receiver, only to discover that the smallest change he had was a ten-pound note. He went back to the cab. 'Do you have any coins? . . . swap you ten quid for a ten p.'

Back in the phone booth, he still wasn't having much

luck. The coin kept falling out of the bottom of the machine. 'Do you think you could help me?' he called to the cabbie, 'I can't remember how you operate these bloody things.'

Eventually the two of them reached Heidi's number. She answered.

'I thought you might be interested to know,' Ivo said through the sound of the pips, '. . . that I've just left Linda.'

In his suite in the Beverly Wilshire Hotel, Leofred Plunkett picked up the telephone. 'I want you to try that London number for me again,' he told the operator in a commanding tone, '. . . the one that was engaged last time.'

While the operator beavered away, he leaned back in his easy chair and sipped a glass of ice-cold Krug champagne. Beyond the protection of the air-conditioning, the swimming pool glinted beneath luxuriant palm trees. In the eternal summer of Los Angeles it was difficult to imagine that the season was ending, and in England the days were shortening, starting with a hint of frost in the air . . . Only two day ago *Hang-ups* had scored record ratings as Leofred was written out forever, falling victim to a psychotic patient with a machete in her handbag. The writers had made sure that the blows were all to Caspar's head and face, so that no-one would be in the least surprised when the actor who played him in the new series bore no resemblance at all to Leofred. After all, who wouldn't look completely different after three episodes' worth of life-saving plastic surgery?

'. . . Hello? . . . Heidi, it's me, Leof. How are you? I'm just fine, great . . . what do you mean, I sound different? . . . anyhow, the reason I'm calling is that I'm just about to fly back from LA, and I'm going to shoot through London on my way back to Cambridge. Why don't I take you out to dinner? . . . Right, will do. I'll get in touch.'

Leofred buzzed reception. 'Have the limousine standing by to take me to the airport. And have someone take my bags down, please.'

'Right away, Mr Plunkett . . .'

A small group of fans was waiting on the sidewalk as he left the hotel. He hastily donned a pair of shades, but it was too late; they had already recognised him.

'It's Fred Plunkett!' they shrieked, 'from *Hang-ups!*'

He signed autographs while the driver loaded his cases into the limousine, and waved to the crowds as they drove away. At LAX he was ushered immediately into the VIP lounge, surrounded by an entourage of airline staff and 'pre-boarded'. Champagne and cigars were waiting for him as he claimed his first-class seat.

'Excuse me, don't I know you?'

Leofred opened his eyes as the whine of the engines died away to a hum. And there, in the seat next to him, was none other than Hilary Ardent, heart-throb of St Godbore's College. She flicked her golden hair back from her lightly tanned cheeks, her foxy features more animated then he remembered.

'I expect you saw me around Cambridge – ' he began modestly.

'No, I mean don't I know you from the television? . . .' She peered at him more closely. '*I* know! You're the guy from that amazing soap opera about the shrink. The one with the doll in it. I hear it's going out in England soon, on Channel Four.'

She extended her hand and squeezed his in a cool, caressing embrace. Her lashes gave a flirtatious little flutter. 'My name's Hilary Ardent. I've been over to LA to visit my godmother – she's a literary agent. I'm going back to start the new term at university. I'm at Cambridge.'

'I know,' said Leofred patiently. 'I'm at the same college.'

'*Really?*' gasped Hilary. 'Are you *sure*? That's amazing! How come we haven't met?'

Leofred just smiled to himself and waved to the stewardess to bring more champagne.

Hilary was now leaning heavily against his arm. ' . . . I suppose you were too busy with your TV career to take any notice of little old me. Your show's a smash hit in the States, you know, *everyone* watches it. They'll be *green* at St Godbore's when they know you're a friend of mine. Listen, let's meet up when we get back. You must come round for a drink. Or better still, I'll hold a dinner party for you. No, a cocktail party . . .'

Heidi put down the phone, feeling slightly puzzled. Leofred did not sound like Leofred at all. She had never heard him so sure of himself, so confident. Still, no doubt all would be revealed.

As soon as she had hung up, the phone rang again.

'It'sh Charles . . .' He sounded distinctly the worse for alcohol. 'Been trying you all evening, but your bloody phone's been engaged – '

'What do you want, Charles?'

'I thought you might be interested to know . . .' He paused for dramatic emphasis. ' . . . that I've just left Joy.'

She smiled. 'Congratulations . . . Goodbye . . . I said, goodbye Charles.'

Heidi lay back on the bed, waiting. She hugged her eyeless bear close to her chest, and closed her eyes.

A little while later, there were footsteps outside and a knock on the door. She opened it.

'Hello, Pig-Face.'